THE STORY OF A MODERN WHORATIO ALGER

Grant Tracy Saxon bares his private life as a stud-for-hire. His career as a hustler began when he dashed out of the arms and bed of his buddy's mother. He was just 15, but especially well-endowed for one so young. He practiced hard, learned quickly—and loved his work!

Read this exciting story of an upright young man who found it useful to stay that way, who is proud of doing his own thing for profit and pleasure, who loves his intimate contact with people of either sex. Meet a satisfied, satisfying man.

THE HAPPY HUSTLER

THE HAPPY
HUSTLER

My Own Story

by Grant Tracy Saxon

**WARNER
PAPERBACK
LIBRARY**

A Warner Communications Company

WARNER PAPERBACK LIBRARY EDITION
First Printing: March, 1975
Second Printing: June, 1975
Third Printing: August, 1975

Front cover photograph by Jerry West

Warner Paperback Library is a division of Warner Books, Inc.,
75 Rockefeller Plaza, New York, N.Y. 10019.

 A Warner Communications Company

Printed in the United States of America

Not associated with Warner Press, Inc. of Anderson, Indiana

Dedicated to:

Mike, Mark, Mack, and the others who thought
it was a damned good idea.

AUTHOR'S NOTE:

The events in this journal all happened, the people are all very real. For obvious reasons, the names have been changed, and although it was necessary, I really rather preferred the real names as opposed to the fictitious ones. And if any of the names I have dreamed up coincide with real live breathing people, accept my apology; it is pure coincidence.

PROLOGUE

"Tracy, honey," a beautiful older woman said to me, lifting my head from its place between her legs.

"What?"

She ran her hands through my hair. "I gotta tell you something. You're the greatest lay I've ever had. I love the way you do my clit with your tongue. . . ."

I went back to doing it.

But she lifted my head again and said, "Do it now, put it in me!"

I obeyed orders eagerly. After a little humping we slowed down because I knew she liked to take it real slow and build to a tremendous climax. In the middle of it, when I thought she was concentrating nice and hard on the nice, hard thing I was sliding in and out of her, she said, "Hey, would you speak at my daughter's school about hustling? They've got a prostitute already, but it could be interesting if . . ."

Try keeping an erection through *that*.

No, I didn't speak at any school. But I do want to say this:

Women do not necessarily have a monopoly on the "oldest profession in the world." There are call girls, sure, a hell of a lot of them, but there are also *call boys*. My name is Grant Tracy Saxon. And I'm one of them.

Perhaps I'm the best of them, because over the years I've been able to compare notes, I've been able to take a good hard look (if you'll pardon the expression) at who I am and what I do and see how it racks up with the others in my particular profession, with the competition. Today, for all practical purposes, you would have to call me a madam, though I don't much like applying the word to the male of the species, but no one has yet invented a better one.

The male of the species. The female of the species. I make it with both, I'm truly bisexual. But I think it's only fair to tell you the truth, I mean the inner feelings, deep down inside—and the truth is I could do without men if I had to, but I couldn't live without women. I don't know why that is, and I don't pat myself on the back because of it nor am I ashamed of it. I think it has something to do with the fact that I once fell in love, really in love, with a girl named Shelley; it was the most beautiful and painful experience of my life. Physical love blended with emotional love for the first time, and though it may never happen again the way it did with Shelley, I know only with a woman could the future possibility of such an affair arise. You'll hear about Shelley and more on my sexual preferences later—let's get back to today:

I'm head of the biggest call-boy ring in the country, and if I boast about it, well, it's because I'm proud of where I am and what I do. But more than tell you about what I do *today,* I want to tell you how I made it in this line of work, what started me off in the first place, what kept me going when the chips were down, and why I love it só.

And I do. Love it. Hustling, that is. You wonder what hustling is, exactly. Same as hooking, only it's a guy selling his body instead of a woman. Any way you cut it, we're prostitutes, and if we're good at it, if we're worth the top money which some of us command, it's a hell of a satisfying job. Come to think of it, even if a kid is just starting out, tricking for five-dollar blow jobs, and he makes his customer feel good, then he's already satisfied—

8

and if he can keep his shit together (which isn't easy) he's starting out in one hell of a damned good and rewarding line of work.

You didn't know there were male prostitutes? Well, you do now, and you're going to know *a lot* about them by the time you finish this. Senators, Congressmen and their wives, airline pilots and stewardesses, a Vegas entertainer whose shows conclude with a pile of panties and bras on the stage (tossed there by adoring matrons), an actress twice nominated for the Oscar—they've all used my stud service.

I could go on and on, and I will, but that comes later. I think the best place to start is at the beginning. Last week, a stunning but rather overweight black lady, a regular customer of mine for two years now, said, "Tracy, honey, you's duh bes' damn stud on dis here earth!" (She likes to put on a heavy accent when she's with me —her whole scene is pretending she's a slave and I'm a northern soldier.) I was flattered, of course, but others have said as much countless other times. What was different about her was that when we were finished with our session, she asked if I would stay and talk with her for a few minutes. "Sure, Flora," I said, and crossed my legs on the bed, ready to listen. She told me she had just read a book written about and by one of the big madams of New York, and she wondered why in hell I hadn't written *my* story.

I thought about it. Why hadn't I written my story? God, I've read enough books in my twenty-seven years, and written a few cheap "pornies" in my spare time, for a few extra bucks and a few extra kicks. But to tell the honest story of my career? I had never really given it much thought.

And I'm not going to *think* about it now either; I'm going to sit here and write it all down.

Flora, I'm going to have to miss next week's session because I'll be pecking away at the typewriter, but hopefully the following week your handsome northern soldier

9

will be able to bring you the first chapter of what has been, for all its ups and downs, a damned happy life!

Grant Tracy Saxon
February, 1974
Chicago, Illinois

CHAPTER ONE

How It All Began

think the very first time I sat down and thought, really thought, about where I had come from, my parents (such as they were), my childhood, all that shit one takes for granted, was in a lousy jail cell in Los Angeles. I was in the tank (for the first time) with a junkie homosexual hustler, and we had little in common except the fact that we both had been picked up for the same offense—oral copulation. Not with each other, for Christ's sake, with our own individual rich tricks, who had somehow vanished on the way to the station. I imagine the guys paid the cops off and there we were, stuck, broke, hungry, and probably still horny. I'm always horny. That's why I'm good at what I do. I think I was born with a hard-on.

The point is, that's what we talked about, or at least what I talked about. The other guy was wrecked out of his mind—hell, he didn't know if he was in prison or the Beverly Hills Hotel—and kept asking me to tell him the story of my life. I don't think I had ever talked about it with anyone before that, mainly because it wasn't anyone's business, and I don't think anyone ever asked.

But this tramp wanted to know where I'd come from, why I ended up where he was, were we alike? I never was able to find out how "alike" we were, because they came for me right after I finished telling him the saga of Grant Saxon to the point where I flew to Los Angeles and boarded the bus for that mythological kingdom of fame and fantasy, Hollywood. Hooray for Hollywood. That's where I got put in the can.

So how did I come to be arrested for sucking a guy's cock in the front seat of his Rolls Royce at three in the morning just outside the doors of Hollywood High? Ridiculously enough, it began with a woman offering me ten bucks if I would pull down my pants and let her do to me precisely what I had been doing to the dude in the Rolls.

Life's a big fucking circle.

I've wondered if I was born with a big dick or if it just grew that way. I know, I know, we all like to dream, and in this age of hot-shot *macho* numbers, men like to add a few inches to their endowments, at least when they talk about themselves. In my case, there are enough photographs of my cock around the world in many private and some not-so-private collections, so lying wouldn't do me any good. Eight inches, hard, is enough to titillate, and it's the God's truth. It also helps when you're a hustler, just as good boobs will help a female prostitute. So right off the bat you know what's down between my legs; it's the thing that's guided me through most of my life, so I thought I'd mention it first.

Secondly, I should pay homage to the two wonderful folks who brought you this little wonder in the first place, who put their genes together and came up with *me*. Virginia and the sometimes-Reverend Robert Saxon were nice, quiet people, typical of the folks who lived and worked in southern Wisconsin. We owned a little house near Lake Geneva, which is really a lake and almost a town, and I can remember life there being as dull as I would imagine it to be in Siberia. At least our summers were hot. (It's funny, I was back in Lake Geneva just a few weeks ago, at the big Playboy Club Hotel there, working a convention!)

During the winters, Dad worked for the highway department, doing everything from plowing country roads to digging cars out of ditches; during the summer he and Mom ran a little "chapel" for the tourist trade, and they cleaned up. I think my basic instinct for hustling came

12

from them—I watched with wide eyes as they counted the take from the collection baskets after each service.

Virginia and Robert were held in high regard by the people who knew them, and their little church was well attended, mainly because Dad knew how to throw a sermon at them without intimidating them and Mom worked a little sex appeal into her organ playing. They were actors more than preachers, and they put on a damn good show, Mom with her high necklines and genteel manner, Dad with his conservative suit, his low-key tone and stance.

Hah! You should have seen them at night, as I often did when I peeked into their room to see what that damned squeaking was. There they were, practicing hell and damnation itself, Mom's legs up in the air, her long skirt around her neck, Dad plugging her, his pants still around his ankles. Amazing, truly amazing. The bedsprings made so much noise, I wanted to oil them.

I don't know how old I was when I first realized what was going on, eight or nine I suppose, but I knew I was a little more *interested* than repulsed. Sure, what they were doing was everything they warned the congregation not to do, but for some reason it seemed to excite me, their hypocrisy, their nonpractice of what they preached. I remember my little cock automatically getting hard, and rubbing it, as I did, sent a wonderful sensation through my body. I wondered if Dad was feeling that same feeling while Mom was on her knees in front of him, taking his thing into her mouth. He sure looked as though it felt good!

Well, it happened all the time, and I began to believe that's what their lives were all about—*sex*. Preaching was incidental, profitable, fun. Dad was husky and liked the outdoors, so the work in the winter pleased him— or got him hot enough to come home and throw a good screw into Mom. Nymphomania runs in the family. The Saxons are sex-happy, any way you slice it.

Then the time came when they wanted me to join the act. I was thirteen, cute, sliding from that wonderful world known as boyhood to puberty, and they figured

13

I'd be an asset to the church during the summers. Besides, what else did I have to do? Go swimming and fishing?

I'd rather be Huck Finn than Marjoe Gortner any day. So I refused to get up there on Sunday and tell the good folks who had gathered to drop their dollar bills in the till that God would strike them dead should they do "naughty" things on their vacations. Let Mom and Dad do that. And as the last "amen" was heard ringing in the church, Virginia would already be hiking her skirts in the back room, and the Reverend Robert pulling out his dong to throw one into her before they went around front to greet the parishioners and wish them a good week.

Not your run-of-the-mill parents. Oh, they weren't so bad, actually. I mean they provided for me, saw to it that I had a decent (and indecent, in the case of peeking in their bedroom door) education, kept me happy. But I always wished I had been closer to them—which would have happened had they been honest with me. So they were sex fiends, so what? Why did they pretend to hate sex? Why did they teach me (as well as their congregation) that sex was dirty? Mom would be sitting at the organ bench playing "Nearer My God To Thee" and Dad's cum would still be running down her leg. Were they so dumb as to think I didn't pick up on what was going on? Maybe so, maybe not, I'll never know. All I know is we could have been closer had they told me the truth about things. Things like sex.

So I had to find other ways to learn.

Boy, did I find other ways.

A kid named Kent showed up with his mother for a summer at Lake Geneva, and they started attending Sunday services regularly. I met him down by the lake one afternoon and asked if he wanted to go out fishing with me and he said yeah, he'd like that.

He was a year older than me (I was fifteen then, he was a worldly sixteen) and seemed to delight in the fact that I had never had a sexual experience except for masturbation, which I had discovered a few months before; I

14

mean real masturbation, where I was able to come. Not much, but it was starting. And it seemed that my cock was growing larger and larger each day, which also pleased me. I had always wanted one as big as Dad's.

Kent was one hell of a seasoned kid. I often wonder why he ended up married to a ditzy broad, father of four brats, and living in Iowa. He could have made a fortune as a hustler. . . .

Anyhow. Kent asked me if I had ever seen dirty pictures. "Sure, of course," I said. I had never seen more than a yellowed photograph of an ugly woman with tits hanging down past her ankles.

"I have lots of them."

"Does your mother know?" I asked.

"Nope. I hide them." He pulled a little packet out of his jeans. "These are only some of them. I'll sell you one if you want."

"Why?" I asked, taking the packet from him, forgetting all about fishing.

" 'Cause I like you," he said, and I could tell by the look in his eyes that he really meant it. I had made a friend.

And my friend's pictures were terrific! Shots of women and men, women and boys, girls and older men, single shots, and even one of a dog fucking a woman. My cock was practically ripping through my pants as I stared breathlessly at them. "How . . . how much does one cost?" I gasped.

"Five bucks."

He *was* a hustler! Five bucks for one lousy picture! Oh, but the endless hours of pleasure that photograph was to give me! I chose one of a beautiful woman sitting on a big cock, with it stuck way up her pussy, and sucking two teenage boys at the same time, from either side of her face. It was truly amazing, and I think the boat rocked when I came to it. I also wanted to buy one of a woman with a flashlight stuffed up her cunt, but I couldn't afford it at those prices.

The following Sunday I ripped off five bucks from the collection and slipped it to Kent outside the little church. He winked.

15

It was the beginning of a beautiful, and sometimes loving, friendship.

Here's what happened, and how his mother figures into my going into prostitution:

I was sitting behind a tree, in the forest beyond the little church and house, with my pants down to my ankles, holding the picture in my left hand, shakily, and beating my cock with my right hand. As I stared at it, my erection seemed to grow bigger and bigger. It had never felt so good, so wonderful! I concentrated on the picture and let my mind wander . . . thinking I was one of the kids standing there getting my dick sucked by the beautiful woman. . . .

"Hey, Grant!"

My heart did a leap and I came back to earth, trying desperately to pull my pants up over the thing sticking out between my legs. But I caught my breath when I realized it was Kent.

"Hey, don't be so scared, no one's coming!" he said, sitting down next to me.

"Wow, you really scared me, wow!" I was still trying to pull my pants up but he stopped me.

"Jesus, but you got a big one," he said.

I did? How the hell did I know? I had never seen any other kids my own age, naked I mean, to really compare. And when I did see other guys in gym class or in the locker room at the pool, we all looked rather alike because we were all soft. But, I was soon to find out, being hard made the difference. A guy's cock can be five inches long when soft, and grow to a mere six inches when hard. Or it can be three inches soft, and rise to a raging ten inches when it gets erect. The soft penis has no relation to the hard penis, something I've had to convince my customers of when they would see one of my boys in a flaccid state. Later, when they'd come out after a session, he or she would say, "My, but he was a *big* one!"

In my own case, I look small when I'm soft, but then I get long and thick, which has been good for business, but that comes later. . . .

Kent talked me into pulling my pants back down to

16

my ankles, all the time staring at my hard cock, telling me he had never seen such a big dick on a kid younger than him. "I'll bet you're as big," I said, or something like that, just to get him to show me his. *You show me yours and I'll show you mine.*

He did. He unzipped and down went the pants and undershorts and out popped an already-half-hard dick, which he quickly fingered into erection, and it turned out that I was a little bit longer than he was, but his was just as thick. So he reached out and touched mine and I touched his and we giggled, and then we started looking at the picture I was still holding and he asked if I wanted to beat off. "Both of us?" I questioned.

"Sure."

"Why not?"

And so we did. We knelt there, facing each other, finally dropping the picture to the grass because we were staring at the tips of our cocks, which were rubbing against each other. I was new at this sort of thing, and he was an expert, or so he seemed, and there was a certain thrill that he could get so excited by being with me, doing that with me. "Your cock is so big, Grant," he kept saying, and I liked hearing it.

I finally put my hand on his shoulder and he shivered and whispered, "I'm gonna shoot," and as soon as the words were out, his cockhead covered mine with creamy white fluid.

And then I saw stars and my cock did the same.

After we had zipped up and laughed about it and promised to do it again sometime, we started back toward the church. And standing there in the yard, under God and all the trees, were Virginia and the Reverend Saxon, along with Mrs. Reynauld, Kent's mother.

Kent and I both turned red. We figured they had seen what we had done down by the lake and we were in for a good lecture, if not a good swift kick in the ass.

No such thing. Mom said, "Well, we've been wondering where you two had gone off to!"

"Fishing?" Dad asked.

I shook my head. "No, just sitting down by the water."

17

Mom smiled at me and said, "Mrs. Reynauld has invited us to dinner tomorrow evening, isn't that nice?"

I looked at Kent and said, "Great."

Dinner, I figured, would be held at the cabin Elizabeth Jane Reynauld and her son had rented nearby, on the edge of the lake. But instead it was at their home in Milwaukee, which, when judged next to our house adjoining the church, was a mansion. They even had *servants*! "You never told me you were rich," I whispered to Kent just before dinner was served.

"Does it matter?" he asked back.

It would, later.

If Elizabeth Jane Reynauld had anything, it was style. Her food was served with style, and it was delicious. The furnishings of the huge house were the kind I'd only read about in fiction. After dinner we retired to the living room, where a fire had been lit in the fireplace (even though it was summer), and Kent played the piano for us. And he was damned good. (I made it a point, years later, when I was running a "house" in Chicago, always to keep a boy on who could play the piano—it made for very good business!)

Then my parents began to talk business with Kent's mother, business which would eventually change my life, business which would take me away from Virginia and Robert forever. Mrs. Reynauld, being "religious" since her hubby croaked on her a few years earlier, wanted to do something for humanity. Picking my parents to lead an evangelical crusade through the South hardly seemed like doing something for humanity, but then I guess there were worse things she could have done with her money. So while she cajoled my father into giving up the snow plowing for preaching in Georgia on her money and in her tent, Kent and I went up to his room to "play."

I use the word *play* because that's exactly what Mrs. Reynauld said: "Why don't you two boys go upstairs and play while we talk business?"

Now, I ask you, what can a fifteen-year-old boy and a sixteen-year-old boy play with, other than each other?

18

We went to Kent's room, locked the door, and I felt my cock getting hard immediately.

"Take off your pants," Kent said.

I blinked, but was I going to argue? I was becoming one hell of a sexed-up little kid! The session I'd had with him the day before, beating off together there in the grass, had left me with an insatiable desire to do it again —or even more. I looked into Kent's eyes and something told me to trust him, for he knew what he was doing.

"Ever fuck a girl?" he asked as I unbuckled my pants. I told him I hadn't even touched a girl.

"Ever had your cock sucked?"

I dropped my shorts and my young dick sprang up. The words alone nearly made me shoot off. I told him I dreamed of it all the time, ever since I had seen Virginia doing it to Robert, but it had never happened.

"Would you like to have your cock sucked?"

What a question. I was dying for it. "Sure," I said, trying to sound matter-of-fact because I sensed what was coming.

Sure enough. The next thing I knew he was kneeling in front of me, taking my dick in both hands, pulling on it. It was rigid. "Are you really fifteen?" he whispered.

"Yes . . . fif . . . fifteen!" I was going crazy with desire —desire to see what the hell it felt like!

"You've got the biggest prick of any kid I've ever seen," he said, and then clamped his mouth over the end of my cock.

The sensation I felt then is one I would feel so many times later, and one I will probably feel for the rest of my life. But in that first moment it was indescribable, sensational. It was a feeling I had never before felt, an excitement I never dreamed possible. It was as if all the tension in my body had been concentrated into one spot —my cock and balls.

He was good. Of course, I had nothing to compare him to, but I sensed he really knew what he was doing. A year or so later I realized he had been as good as the best chick I had come across, and to this day I don't think anyone has ever sucked my cock (and there have been thousands on their knees before me) better than Kent.

So I just stood there, feeling weak in the knees, while he worked on me. I tried holding back, wanting to prolong the sensation as much as possible, but I couldn't. Almost without a sound, without a warning, I came. What happened was, I started to think of the picture he had sold me, the one I now carried in the "secret" compartment of my wallet, and I felt my entire body shaking. I started spurting and looked down, and to my surprise he kept sucking, drinking all of my sperm down into his throat.

There was something about this orgasm which was different from the others I'd had—I felt more like a man. I thought there was more sperm than usual, that it lasted a longer time, and that it was wilder, more exciting than it ever had been. I had grown up! I was a man now! I had had my cock sucked!

No big deal, huh? Well, to the son of a preacher from southern Wisconsin who froze his ass all winter and suffered from boredom all summer, it was quite an experience. I fell to the bed, collapsing, thrilled, the biggest grin ever on my face.

Kent sat next to me on the bed. There was a big dribble of white sperm on his chin. I stared at it in awe—it was mine! I was fascinated, utterly fascinated. It was just like the woman in the photograph he had sold me. And what was even more fascinating about it was the fact that I felt no guilt, that, despite Dad's warnings against "sins of the flesh" and especially "those who couple with their own sex," I didn't feel the least bit unnatural. I had enjoyed it, actually, and Kent had too. So what was wrong with it?

My hard-on went down and we started talking. I wanted to know about sex, everything and anything he had to tell. He told me he had a girlfriend and he described in detail (while fingering his cock through his pants) how he screwed her. I asked him where he had learned to give a blow job and he told me his older cousin had been doing it to him ever since he was about twelve—his first orgasm (by means other than masturbation) had been in a guy's mouth, just as mine had

20

been. He also said his girl wouldn't take his dick in her lips, but he was working on it. Then he asked me if I wanted to see more dirty pictures.

The kid was a sex maniac at sixteen! And there I was, Grant, the preacher's son, wanting to be the same.

He pulled a shoe box from the back of his clothes closet. "Mom never looks in here because I used to keep a pet snake behind my shoes. She thinks it may still be there." He opened the box and lifted a wad of tissue paper. Under it was a rolled-up magazine with a few words printed in French on the cover. Then, when he opened the magazine, my eyes bulged out of my head.

There, in living color, before my young and eager eyes, was a guy and a girl. He was sitting on the edge of the bed, his big hard cock in one hand. She was standing next to him, with one foot up on the bed, her pussy opened wide. Her big tits sat pointed on her chest and there was a big smackeroo of a smile on her face. (On mine, too!)

Kent turned the page and I felt my cock growing harder and harder. The guy in the photo had turned a bit, and the girl's smooth ass was facing the camera. You could see his cock standing up still, but his face was buried between her legs and his hands were spreading her buttocks apart. "God," I said, never having seen Dad do that to Mom. I was receiving a crash course in sex education which I' would find very useful in a very short time to come and with Kent's own mother, of all people!

Picture after picture, sexual position after sexual position—I was getting dizzy! "Let's beat off," Kent finally suggested—either that or I was going to come in my pants!

So I suddenly became very brave and said, "Take off your pants," to him, just the way he had ordered me to do the same. So he slipped his shoes off, then his pants and shorts, and knelt on the bed with me. The magazine was down in front of us and we glanced at it as we masturbated frantically.

"This is my favorite," he said when we came to a picture of the girl kneeling in front of the guy. She had her mouth open and a long spurt of jism was shooting from the head of his cock into her mouth, hitting the tip of her tongue. Her face was already covered with cum. "Oh, Christ!" Kent said; he was very into oral sex.

"Ohhhhh," I moaned, as any kid that age would. And I practiced that moan again and again in the many years to come, when it was false but useful—when my trick is needed a little vocal urging to get them off.

"Hold off," Kent whispered, "hold off till I'm ready!" He kept flipping through the pages and suddenly I saw something that completely blew my mind—the girl getting it in the ass! He was fucking her in the ass, "Greek style," as we would later call it in the trade. It amazed me—it had never crossed my mind—and turned me on all the more.

Then I saw a photo of the girl with a finger all the way up the guy's anus and he looked as though he was obviously enjoying it. Then I felt Kent's hand wrap around the shaft of my cock and I looked up. "Take mine, let's beat each other off," he said, and I wrapped my fingers around the first penis I had ever touched, other than my own. It was strangely exciting—I mean, it felt pretty much the same, but it belonged to someone else!

Then he turned the page and I remember the picture vividly—the girl had her face, her pretty face, stuck between the guy's hairy ass cheeks. Honestly, she was sucking his asshole, sliding her tongue in and out, or so I supposed. It was another position I would find useful in the years to come. Man, what an education I was getting there on that bed.

I froze, knowing I couldn't hold off for anything any longer, and looked down to see Kent's hand pulling on my cock. Suddenly it started to shoot, and the first spurt of cum shot halfway across the room.

"Oh, God, oh, Jesus," he moaned, and then the same thing happened to him, like gunfire. His bed was soon covered with our sperm, the book was full of splotches, and our hands were drenched.

"Fuck, oh fuck," he groaned as we collapsed into a

giggling heap on the bed. I didn't know what to do with my creamy hand, I was laughing so hard because it had been so wonderful, and the next thing I knew Kent was licking all of his jism off my fingers, sucking them. I could hardly believe it. And as if that were not enough, he dipped his head between my legs and took my half-hard dick in his mouth again and started sucking it clean.

Now do you see why I wonder how in the hell he ended up with a wife and four kids, selling insurance? Christ. And he was so damned handsome!

Maybe I should mention something here about my bisexuality. I'm not going to apologize for it—on the contrary, I'm going to flaunt it. You see, after having lived sex for the last thirteen years, I think I know something about the basic sexual drive in man. And I believe that everyone is basically bisexual. It doesn't take a hell of a lot to get a guy to "try it" with another guy if you're in the right situation at the right time. For example, take a three-way, two guys and a girl—doesn't the law of averages tell you that the guys are bound to touch each other now and then in the course of the menage love-making and that they don't turn into monsters because of it?

Most call boys are bisexual. No, perhaps that isn't true; *most* call boys are *homo*sexual. A *great many* of them are *bi*sexual. And only a few are straight, tried-and-true "women studs" who find it hard in the profession because first of all they have the competition of the boys who are bisexual and will fuck the women who are their potential clients, and secondly, because they do not swing both ways, they find even less security than most call boys. Sometimes a kid will find himself a handsome old dowager who becomes his "old lady"—only until she sees a prettier one and dumps him. I know, it happened to me.

There is no other word for it, I am a madam, and like my female counterparts, I'm bisexual. I can't survive on only one sex. If I'm off for a week with a special lady who pays well for my services, I find myself longing for

23

a cock, and will occasionally slip off conveniently with a bellhop or some other cute boy and have a quickie. Same thing in reverse. If a gentleman has acquired my services, taking me, say, on a vacation to the Bahamas, I'll no doubt end up spending an hour of our five days together shacking up with a woman just to remind myself what pussy feels like (not to mention the extra fifty bucks I may have gained).

To remind myself what pussy feels like—that's not exactly true. It's really because I can't stand going without a woman for very long, meaning my homosexual desires are not nearly as strong as my heterosexual ones. Homosexuality is a phase most boys go through when they are young, and that is precisely what I was going through with Kent, but in some ways I never came out of it, and I'm glad of that. Yes, I added women to my interests, as you will see, and now find making love to females even more satisfying than men, as I've already told you. But had I shed sexual interest in men (I guess I couldn't have, even had I tried), I would never have become what I am today.

A word to all you straight guys out there reading this: try it. You may like it. And you may not. But at least you've opened yourself up enough to see what it's like, and you haven't lost anything. I think most women are willing to try it with another woman, so why not men doing the same? Enough on that. Getting back to Kent . . .

We were giggling like two little schoolboys (isn't that what we were, really?) when our mothers, simultaneously, called our names from downstairs. "Coming," we answered, which is exactly what we had been doing. We cracked up again, and finally got into our pants and shoes and looked at each other with a new kind of trust that comes with friendship, a friendship that was to last through the years. (Yes, I buy insurance from him today!)

Just before we descended the stairs I asked, "Kent?"

"Yeah?"

"Can we do it again sometime?"

"Hell, yes."

That was good enough for me.

A week later I was spending the *night* at their house, and as Mom and Dad were signing papers with Mrs. Reynauld—they had decided to go on the tour of the Bible Belt, God bless 'em—Kent told me he had a "secret" and we ran to the big oak tree in front of the house and I asked what it was. I knew it had something to do with sex.

"You saw our maid, Connie?" He had this big grin on his face.

"Yes," I answered.

"I walked into the garage the other day and caught her with Mother's chauffeur."

Caught her? Doing what? Every dirty thought imaginable flipped through my head. I don't think I said anything, I just stood there like some dummy with his tongue hanging out, waiting for the rest of the juicy story he was obviously going to take his time in telling.

"She was holding her skirt up, leaning back against the car, and he was fucking her like crazy."

"Honest to God?" I remember asking that, and when he nodded I sat down under the tree, ready for every exciting little detail, but mainly because my cock was getting hard in my pants and straining my underwear— by sitting down I could rub it as he talked.

He fell to his knees and said, "Shit, they froze! They stopped, with his cock still in her, and just stared at me, scared shitless! I guess they were sure I would tell Mother, and she's so religious . . ."

"Okay, but what happened? What did they do?" I didn't want to know about his mother being religious. Hell, so was mine!

"They fucked for me."

"Fucked *for* you?"

"Fucked for me. I slammed the door and stood in front of it and told them I wanted to watch. Frank pulled his cock out of her and she dropped her skirts and they were both talking at once, but I shut them up."

"How?"

"I whipped out my dick."

"Did you fuck her?" I was dying to hear about that—I could picture it! I even looked in the direction of the garage. I could see Kent standing there with his pants down around his ankles fucking Connie while she had her skirt in her mouth. . . .

"Don't rush me," he said, leaning against the tree, one hand between his legs, rubbing himself, "I want you to hear the whole thing."

"Come on, goddamnit."

"I . . . I told them I wanted them to do just what they were doing when I walked in, I wanted to watch them fuck nice and slow. They started saying things again, but I told them to shut up and start fucking or I'd have Mother bounce them in a minute. So Connie looked down at my dick and started drooling and in a second she was lifting her skirts again and good ol' Frank, he'd fuck a cow if he had to, he shoved it right back in her."

I suddenly had a question. I don't know why it came to me, but I wondered where her panties were. Had she taken them off? Were they on the garage floor, or around her leg, or was he fucking her through them, had they been ripped open or something? What?

He grinned and answered, "She doesn't wear them."

"Holy shit." That turned me on. It really did. I had sat through dinner at their house and everything while Connie the maid served us and greeted us and poured our coffee with nothing on under her little black skirt! Jesus. I nearly shot off in my pants.

"He shoved his dick in and out of her, just like in the pictures I showed you, slow and easy, and she made lots of soft sounds, looking straight at me all the time. And then I even saw his stuff running down her leg. I stuck my head up nice and close and watched him squirt it into her."

"Shiiiiiiiiiiiit!" I squealed, and fell back on the grass, rolling over, kicking my legs in the air. It was too fucking good to be true—and I was so damn jealous I wanted to break his neck. When I sat up again, he was biting on a fingernail as though we were discussing the weather.

"Well?" I asked, wondering if that was the end of the story.

"She sucked me off."

I knocked my head against the tree. "I don't believe it, no, I don't believe a word of it, you asshole!" I believed *every* word of it, that was the trouble. "Was it good?" I finally asked.

"Oh, yeah, I guess so. . . ." He sat there pretending to act nonchalant, the creep, so I socked him and we grappled around on the grass for a minute or two, laughing like crazy, feeling each other's hard-ons straining inside our pants, and then we let go of each other and tried to relax a bit. "Hey," he said.

"What?"

"I think it was the best blow job I've ever had."

"What about the chauffeur?"

"Frank? He was still fucking her when she bent down to gobble me, and then he pulled out and just stood there with his mouth open. He's an asshole anyway. And she's a little nuts herself. She sucked me till I came and then she started crying and all, pretending we had forced her into it, but she was pretending. I know she's been hot ever since she started working for us. She loved it—in fact, I think she loved getting caught. I thought I heard her trying to peek into the bathroom a few times when I was taking a bath."

"Jesus." I guess it was the apt thing for a preacher's son to mutter.

"Now I have control over them."

I didn't understand, and he could tell by my puzzled expression.

"See, I can tell Mother about it and she'll can them, it's that simple. She'd never believe them over me."

"So you can get Connie to do anything you want?"

"Sure can."

I drew a deep breath to keep from thinking about it too much because I knew what would happen in my undershorts. "You're really lucky," I finally said.

"You too."

"What?"

"You know, tonight, at dinner . . . ?"

I nodded. "Yeah, what?"

"Right after, when you were in the living room with your parents and Mother, I heard Connie telling Frank that she had the hots for you."

"M . . . m . . . me?"

"Like that?"

It took me a moment to recover. "Like it? I love it."

"But that's not the surprise."

"What do you mean?"

He started walking back toward the house, but his voice was clear in the late-summer air. "Connie's coming up to our room at midnight."

I was speechless.

And so it happened, folks, at the ripe old age of fifteen-going-on-sixteen, Grant Tracy Saxon lost his virginity—or what was left of it. Connie walked into Kent's bedroom at midnight on the dot and said a soft "Hi," to which we responded the same. I would teach my boys, years later, to always enter a room and utter a pleasant, if somewhat sexy, "Hi," to the waiting customer. Oh, the stuff I learned at the Reynauld mansion!

Connie was an extremely pretty girl of about nineteen, with dark hair and deep green eyes. She seemed a little nervous, which I guess was understandable under the circumstances. I was a bit nervous, too, to say the least. Kent introduced us and she held my hand for a moment, lightly, but with a sexuality I can't describe. Then she sat on the bed, between us, and put her hands on our thighs.

Our cocks were already springing out of our pants.

To break the ice, as it were, she asked Kent, "What would your girlfriend say about this?"

He answered her with an answer. "What would *Mother* say?"

She didn't answer that one, but glanced to make sure she had locked the door.

"Yeah," I added, "what would my parents say?"

Then she said, with a sly smile and a look directly at our crotches, "You have a *point* there."

Then it started happening—her hands moving over

28

our bodies, undressing us, Connie finally falling to her knees, taking out cocks in her mouth, first separately, then at the same time, which was some feat (but something I've been able to master quite well in the years since; Linda Lovelace, eat your heart out!). Then she said it too: "My God, but you have a big cock!" I turned red for a minute. See, at that time I didn't really know I should have been that proud of my equipment. But with all the adoration it had been getting lately, I was starting to realize *I may have an attribute which is rather unique. . . .*

But right then all I could think about was putting it in her. She sucked on our cocks at the same time, for a long time, caressing our balls, licking our swollen heads, moaning, and watching it all with her chestnut eyes. Kent put his arm around me and I could tell by the way he was trembling that he was going to shoot. I figured, what the hell, I may as well do the same.

And so we came together, in her mouth, and I'll be damned if she didn't drink down every last drop. Then she got up as we stood there holding on to each other for dear life, dazed, and flopped on the bed, spreading her legs and lifting her skirt.

And I found myself staring at the first real bare pussy I had ever seen in my life. It certainly was better than watching Virginia through the keyhole, or looking at the magazine Kent had stashed in his closet. This was the real thing, and I was utterly fascinated by it.

We undid her garter belt and pulled her black stockings from her legs and she asked, "What are you children doing to me?" in mock surprise, our cum still on her lips.

Children? We're getting ready to fuck you, that's what we're doing! I found myself staring at her cunt again, just staring. It was somehow forbidding, challenging. It was beautiful, I wasn't sure that it was real. The whole scene seemed like a bizarre dream.

But it was far from a dream—my parents would have called it a nightmare induced by Satan himself, and I knew that for sure the minute I brought my fingertips up and ran them through her pubic hair. It felt very differ-

29

ent from my own, different from Kent's, too. Ours was thick and wiry; hers was downy soft. I ran my finger over the lips of her cunt. They were thick and seemed to be made of layers. They were damp and very, very warm. I looked up at Kent with such a fascinated expression he had to laugh. My cock was ready to explode.

"Oh, that feels so nice," Connie finally purred, pulling me into place on top of her.

Kent reached out and patted me on my buttocks, probably for good luck. I didn't need it. I felt like King Kong at that point.

Finally we got her sweater open and her tits out, and we both sucked them as she moved my cock into place with her hand. It happened quickly, and yet in retrospect I can recall every detail—how hot her pussy felt as I entered it for the first time, how the walls seemed to hug my cock, the moans she made from deep in her throat, the sheer ecstasy of feeling her body jolt when I was all the way in her, and the thunder in my head when she said, over and over again, "Oh, you're so big, you're so big!" My cock couldn't have been more than six or seven inches when I was fifteen; apparently the chauffeur, Frank, had only four inches. Or she couldn't count. Come to think of it, she wasn't the brightest girl in the world.

But that didn't matter; she was a wonderful lay, and, being my first, would always hold a piece of my heart. A small piece, mind you, because I've given it away countless times, but a piece nonetheless. I've fallen in love a few times, you see. You might call me "the male whore with the heart of gold."

After I came—when I did, I thought I had passed out or died or fallen off a cliff—I pulled out and let Kent fuck her, lubricating his cock with my hot, wet cum. And Connie seemed to love it. While he was screwing her he asked me to put a finger up his ass, something which I, again, have done many times since, often to the surprise of my customers, who seem to find it a new and exciting diversion. You'd be surprised how many people there are walking this earth who think their anus is for one use only.

When Kent had finished the three of us sat there, famished. Then he started licking her pussy—he loved to lick up cum, anywhere and everywhere—until his face was all wet. I said, "Your face is shining."

"I'm shining all over," he replied.

And then we relaxed some more, until Connie asked Kent, "Do you do that to him?"

"Do what to him?"

"Suck his peter?"

"Sure," Kent said almost defensively, "why not? He's my pal."

"Most guys won't do that," she said.

"They're afraid," Kent said. He really had his shit together for a sixteen-year-old kid.

Connie smiled and confessed. "You know, I've always wanted to do it with another girl or a woman. I really would like that."

The thought of it excited me—and Kent, too. "I'd like to watch that," he said.

I nodded in agreement.

Little did I know that years later I'd watch so much of *that* it would put me to sleep!

Mom and Dad got into show biz, and I got into Liz. Yes, folks, Elizabeth Jane Reynauld. And this is how that evolved:

The Reverend Saxon boarded up his church for the winter as soon as the tourist season ended, and Virginia began packing for the long tour of tent shows in the warm southern states, a tour that would take them into another tax bracket.

Where was little Grant all this time? Well, I'd turned a hot sixteen, and I'd spent most of my time with Kent, balling Connie, spying on Kent as he tried to get his girlfriend to suck his cock, beating off—just about everything I did had to do with sex. I was educating myself, fast. Frank was even taking photographs of our wild parties in the Reynauld garage! We were into one hell of a scene out there in the midst of the very rich outskirts of Milwaukee.

But it was time to start school, and what would I do this year? Go from tutor to tutor through the South, a place I feared I would hate? (It must have been a premonition—to this day I detest the South, and every time a trick invites me to fucking Florida, I charge double!) Live at home alone? What?

You guessed it, Elizabeth Reynauld to the rescue. Since Kent and I had become such good friends, such close pals, why didn't I move in for the winter, and my parents could visit at Thanksgiving and Christmas? I didn't think that was such a big deal because nothing had been made of those holidays in the past, at least not in the Saxon household.

But we all loved the suggestion. Virginia and Robert had a place to dump their kid while they went off to fame and fortune selling Jesus on the stump; Elizabeth was seeing her own long-range plan coming into focus, finally; Kent would be near his best pal; Grant Tracy Saxon would continue going to school, with no interruptions, and would be living in a good Christian home as well.

My ass.

Elizabeth Jane Reynauld probably fucked her husband to death, because she was the biggest nymphomaniac who ever lived. And she weighed a lot, too. Honest, the woman was insatiable! By the time she made a pass at me I had pretty much come to know sex—I mean, I was fucking Connie and two other girls regularly, getting it on with Frank (never alone, always with the girls), and, of course, Kent. So I didn't consider myself shockable. But good old Liz, she shocked the living hell outta me.

The reason is, she never let on. She was the good, upright, and uptight (and probably frigid, I thought) mother; she was a woman of God, a woman who gave of her time and of her money (she had plenty of both) to see the word of the Bible brought to many people (via *Virg and Bob's Traveling Salvation Show*). She was a woman who never allowed cursing in her presence, and tolerated drink only during dinner (the very best imported wine).

She kept up that image for a hell of a long time—right

through till my parents came up to Milwaukee for Christmas (they had skipped Thanksgiving, which was all right with me 'cause Connie, Kent, and I had a wild time after the big dinner, when Elizabeth felt she had "gas" and wanted to retire to her room). Christmas was lovely, with a big beautiful tree all trimmed in gold and red, candles burning everywhere in the house. There were gifts for everyone—from Elizabeth, of course. There was food, and there was goodwill, and I remember it as the happiest Christmas of my life. Kind of like the calm before the storm.

When I think back, I guess that special night with Kent *had* to happen when it did, otherwise we never would have been able to express ourselves the way we were allowed to. Certainly, what his mother did the week after Christmas would never have allowed that one night of sheer happiness to exist.

We drove Mom and Dad to the train depot and waved them goodbye. It was two days after Christmas, and they'd had a wonderful time. But I was glad to see them go, for Elizabeth had since become more of a mother to me than my own mother, and I could tell that my father, for all his preaching against the "lure of spirits" and "not allowing the devil to tempt thee to drink," was downing a good fifth of expensive bourbon a day. I didn't like having to witness it; I rather liked knowing they were happy with each other doing the revivals down South.

Driving back to the mansion, I remember a strange silence in the car. Finally Mrs. Reynauld said to Frank, "Careful . . . the snow." It was coming down hard and it was beautiful. I had been born and raised in the Midwest, and I never took the beautiful white stuff for granted. I still liked it.

Kent finally mentioned something (probably groaning) about having to go back to school in a week, and his mother hit us with the first of her attacks: "I've made a decision, Kent darling." Whenever she called him darling, you knew something was wrong.

He asked her what she meant.

She explained something which made absolutely no sense at all, but by the tone of her words we could tell

33

she had made up her mind. Kent was transferring to a private school, an "academy" in northern Wisconsin, which was the school his Uncle Henry had attended. He had died before Kent was even born, for Christ's sake! Elizabeth Reynauld, sitting between the two of us, explained that she knew it would be hard for us to part, but we must think of Kent's college future before friendship. Like I said, it made no sense—switching schools for one semester?—but her mind was made up and there was no changing it.

We rode in silence all the way back to Greenfield. What was there to say?

It was that night, as we walked up the stairs to our rooms, that I realized I loved Kent. Suddenly I knew I loved him because the thought of him leaving made me feel so empty and alone. My parents had gone (had they not gone before I was born?), and now my best friend was going. I loved him and I still do, and it's the kind of love a person can't explain. It has almost nothing to do with sex, it has to do with being human. Yes, I was an impressionable sixteen and I came from a mildly fucked-up background and I probably was *in* love with him for a time there. My God, he was my hold on reality! I worshiped him. And I began to hate his mother for taking him from me.

We stopped at the top of the staircase and looked at each other. "Will you come and sleep with me tonight?" he asked, nearly in tears. I was glad he needed the comfort of my arms, rather than Connie's or one of the other girls he knew.

We went to his room, feeling very tired and lethargic, and crawled into bed. But, beat and depressed, we still found excitement in our bodies, and he put his hand on my cock and I found his. We held each other like that, tightly, communicating our thoughts through bodily contact rather than words (which much of the business later would be like). It was the first moment of my life in which I realized what it was like to love somebody! I hadn't known love—Virginia and Bob hadn't given me love, they had thrown a Bible in front of my face while they finger-fucked each other behind it,

34

and now they were off doing their circus act. Elizabeth had shown affection for me by taking me in as her own son, but that had been done out of sympathy and caring for my parents—and, I knew it and admitted it to myself, as part of a business deal (she deducted a bit of cash from the Bible-act payroll to apply toward my room and board). I didn't know where my grandparents were; I didn't know if I even had grandparents. I had no friends, no enemies. And here was this one person, a boy, a year older than me, who liked me enough to sleep with me, to talk with me, to share his secrets and his girls with me.

I looked into his eyes. "Friends forever," I said.

"I don't want to leave," he murmured, and then caught himself, probably telling himself big boys don't cry. He nodded, finally, and said, "Friends forever."

And then I gulped because I knew what I was going to do and I knew it was wrong and that perhaps he'd be shocked and hate me for it and maybe even hit me. But I knew I was going to kiss him no matter what.

Now it sounds like such a simple thing, kissing another guy. I still won't do it to just anyone, and, what's more, most customers don't expect it nor do they want it. Only sometimes, with young and good-looking men, does it happen, and when it does, it is part of the business deal and nothing more or less. But with Kent it was quite a different story.

And the funny thing was—we talked about it a few years later and realized this—we were thinking the same thing. He was wanting to kiss me, and feeling all the pangs I was feeling. He was worried what I would think if he initiated it! But we both realized that the only way we could show what we felt for one another at that time was by kissing—we had done everything else, what was left that was special and tender?

I closed my eyes and pressed my lips to his. To my surprise, he accepted. Then his lips parted and I felt his tongue in my mouth and I let mine slip into his. We kissed passionately, tears in our eyes, pressing our young bodies together, rubbing our hands along each other's backs as if we were each protecting one another from some terrible storm. We began a rhythm with our bodies—our cocks were hard and rubbing together—and in a few moments semen spurted from both our organs and glued us together. Finally we pulled our lips apart, panting, not uttering a word. I moved my head close to his chest and closed my eyes. We stayed like that for a few minutes, and then I really started to cry.

I couldn't help it. I just lay there, sobbing like a baby. I don't think I had cried since I *was* a baby, and I know I have not cried since. The dam had burst, and Kent did not try to stop my tears. He only held me tightly.

And then, for the first time in my life, I said a prayer which I meant with all my heart and soul. *Please God, don't let me lose this friend.*

And we finally fell asleep. Oh, we shared each other's bodies many times after that, up till the time he got married, sometimes just the two of us, more often with a girl or two. But we never kissed again. We had done it once, and that one time had told us what we had to say, and those unspoken words would last a lifetime.

Often, in the rough and sometimes terrifying times to come, thoughts of that night, of Kent, would become my only solace.

I had a premonition that night in the big black limousine, driving back to Greenfield after we had seen Mom and Dad off at the train depot, that things would never be the same once Kent went off to the academy.

Understatement of the year, Grant.

What happened was, we took him up there and toured the place (I hated it and I could tell he did too—*fuck Uncle Henry and tradition!*) and finally parted. I gave him a big bear hug and said something like, "Take care, buddy," which seemed painless enough.

"I will, I will," he said. Then he turned and kissed his mother lightly on the cheek. "Bye, Mother."

"Goodbye, darling," she said. And we turned and walked away.

Driving home in the car, I put my head back and fell asleep for a few hours. We had not had much sleep the night before, in a hotel in a little city near the academy, and I didn't understand how Mrs. Reynauld could be so alert. She asked Frank to turn the radio on in back and she hummed along with the songs. I dozed.

I was awakened by the smell of gasoline (this is back when it wasn't as precious as gold). I opened my eyes to see we were in a service station, and Mrs. Reynauld was just entering the ladies' room. I stretched and realized that I had an erection. It had happened in my sleep—had she seen it? It plagued my mind for the next few hours. If she had, I was very embarrassed; if she had not, I was damn glad. I started to doze off again, but this time I was smart enough to place my hands between my legs.

I suddenly woke up when I somehow sensed there were three hands down there instead of two. I saw Mrs. Reynauld's hand resting on my thigh. "I'm sorry, Grant, dear. I just wanted to wake you and ask if you're hungry."

"Uh," I muttered, sitting up straight in the mushy seat. "Yeah, I mean, yes, I guess so. Sure."

"Good, because I'm famished." Then she pushed a little button and the window separating Frank from us opened. "Frank, pull into that restaurant we saw advertised just a while back," she ordered, and Frank slowed the big Cadillac down on the icy road.

Her hand was still on my thigh and I was getting a bit nervous because of it.

"Yeah, I sure am hungry," I said, moving slightly, "I could use some food." *Why the hell doesn't she move her hand?*

"Wonder how Kent is doing?" she mumbled, hand still there.

"Fine, fine," I said, "don't worry about him, Mrs. Reynauld."

She turned and faced me and finally took her goddamn hand away. "Liz."

I blinked. "What?"

"Liz. I want you to call me Liz from now on. Frank calls me Mrs. Reynauld, but you call me Liz."

Oh, Christ, what's happening here? "Sure, fine," I said, brushing my hand through my hair.

I thought about it as Frank parked the big car in the

37

lot in front of the restaurant. I had never, since the day I'd met her, heard *anyone* call her Liz!

The meal went smoothly, mainly because I was starving, but there was an overriding sensation, this crazy tension I couldn't explain nor ignore. Something was *different* about her now; in a few short hours something had changed, changed radically. She seemed to be looking at me through different eyes, talking to me with a different tone, and, topping that off, her legs were wrapped around mine under the table.

Was it my powerful imagination—or was Liz Reynauld hot for me?

I had my answer soon enough.

Frank stopped the car in front of the house and we got out. "Frank, remind Connie to wake Grant here at seven. He goes back to school tomorrow."

"Yes, Mrs. Reynauld," Frank said, and got back into the car.

Mrs. Reynauld, shit. LIZ! I waited till she opened the door and then I went in, stomped the little bit of snow from my shoes, said goodnight, and ran up the stairs to my room.

I wondered what other surprises the night would bring. It didn't take long to find out.

I showered, put on a pair of pajamas, and jumped into my big bed. I felt tired after the long drive, after sleeping sitting up, after worrying my way through that meal. I curled up in the pillows, thinking about school again, trying to think positive, *school is going to be great!, I'm not going to miss Kent! . . .*

But Liz Jane Reynauld kept creeping into my thoughts. I thought about having sex with her, but the idea seemed so remote, so silly. She was a beautiful woman and I guess I loved her much the way a son loves a mother, but having sex with her was something I had never considered. Not only would she win the Miss Deep Freeze contest of any year (or so I thought then), she wasn't very liberal—and to fuck your son's best friend you had to be one hell of a liberal broad!

But the more I tried to put it out of my mind, the more I thought about the possibility that it had all been

38

planned—or was I giving myself too much credit? Was I all that attractive at fifteen for her to get rid of my parents and her own son? How long had she been thinking about it? How long had she been counting the days till she could conveniently ship her son off to that lousy academy so she could put the make on his best friend?

I'm nuts, I'm totally cuckoo! I smashed my head down into the pillows and turned over and over, trying to tell myself I was imagining the whole thing, that her legs wrapped around mine under the table at the restaurant had been arthritis or some damn thing. I had been reading too much into everything, I was becoming a sex maniac. So what if she asked to be called Liz? So what if she played footsy a little and it gave me a thrill—a lot of lesser things had given me sexual thrills.

I rolled and turned in bed for almost an hour. I wanted to sleep, knowing I had to be up early for school, but I couldn't—I think I wanted Liz to come to my door! I *expected* it! My ego had been shattered somehow. I got up and paced the room and looked out at the snow falling in the yard, but no one came to the door, and when I finally fell back into bed I felt a bit defeated and disappointed, and drifted into a deep, restless sleep.

Aha! The next thing I knew, a woman's hand was running through my hair. I opened my eyes and found Liz staring down at me. Her face was not quite as beautiful as usual, since most of her makeup had been wiped away, or maybe it was the color of the dark room, of the moon reflecting off the snow. Truth is, she looked like a corpse. She smiled gently, as though she were asking permission.

I nodded. *What's a boy to do?*

Not a word was spoken. I felt her hands move to unbutton the top of my pajamas, and then she roamed my chest and belly with her fingertips, stopping where the bottoms tied, where my pubic hair began. I already knew I had a good body—Kent and I worked out with weights every day—and she loved touching it. And whether she looked like death warmed over or the goddess Diana, her caresses worked magic—my cock stood up, ready.

She kissed my chest and untied my pajama bottoms. I

39

pressed my knees together and lifted my ass from the mattress so she could slip them down over my butt. She did, but they still covered my cock. That's when she stood up in the middle of the room and dropped her robe. She was completely naked, and her body shocked me— I had been used to Connie and other shapely girls, and even when she was not well dressed, Mrs. Reynauld— Liz—looked pretty well put together. But, undressed, it all hung out. Her tits sagged and there was a good roll around her middle. Her pussy looked monstrous. I bit my tongue. But what could I do, order her out? It was her house!

She walked to the bed and with one fast move fell to her knees at the side. She brushed her hair back over her shoulders and looked at the bottom part of my pajamas, where my cock was still hidden.

Then she pulled them down, but without looking, and moved around the foot of the bed and pulled them off. And that's when I heard the gasp, as she got up between my legs and saw what was lying there. I guess she had no idea my cock was so big (it had grown at least another inch in the past six months), because she just stared at it with her mouth open, dumbfounded. It was a look I would grow accustomed to as time went on. But then it perplexed me—was I *that* special? She just kept staring and staring at my dick.

Finally I sat up and took off the top of my pajamas, and fell back, naked, propping myself on my elbows so I could watch her suck me off. And she did. She moved to the bed on her knees, her big tits swinging in front of her, against my legs, and grabbed my cock in her hand and went down on me.

Well, I came near an orgasm really quickly, and I was hoping that would be it, biff, bam, thank you, ma'am, but no, she had other ideas.

"OHHHHHHHHH, GOD!" she screamed as she sat down on my dick. It plunged all the way up her in one fast jolt. I hardly knew what hit me. And all I had to do was lie there and let her ride me. I was terrified (she was a big woman, and what if she should slip and fall on me?) and guilty (she was Kent's mom, for God's sake!)

and yet I remained hard as a rock, as though I had no control over my cock.

She bounced up and down for what seemed like hours, screaming, riding me like a bucking bronco, squealing in delight. And each time I was ready to come, she sensed it and stopped for a second or two till I had calmed down.

But then, just before I came, *she* came, and as she did she yelled, "FUCK ME, KENT, FUCK ME, BABY!"

Kent! She was calling me by her son's name!

I came and twisted my head in agony, not wanting to look at her body on top of mine, and when she finally pulled off me, I rolled over on the pillows and waited till she had left the room. No tears this time, only terror. I knew I had to get out of there, but where could I go? The only person I had in the world was Kent, and I couldn't very well show up on the doorstep of the academy and say, "Look, your mother raped me so I thought I'd come stay with you." Virginia and the Reverend were preaching, drinking, making money, and screwing their way through the Bible Belt. They didn't want me. Where to go?

I had no idea, but I knew the farther from "Liz," the better. I was packed and out of the house before seven, when Connie was to come and wake me for school. Fuck school too—it bored me, to tell the truth. I knew where the train depot was and I had a little money saved, enough to get me to another city at least. Maybe Chicago, maybe farther west, where it was warmer. California was in the back of my mind already—it had been for years, ever since I had seen some travel folders in one of the little hotels in Lake Geneva—but I wasn't consciously thinking of heading there. All I wanted to do was get the hell away from Milwaukee.

I walked part of the way in the snow—no one thought it strange, because I looked like just another kid going to school in the morning—and then I took a bus downtown and walked the few blocks to the Chicago and Northwestern railroad depot. I had enough for a ticket to Kansas City, one way, and that sounded as far away from Milwaukee as China.

I wasn't on the train fifteen minutes when a gorgeous woman in her forties, dressed in a mink coat, offered me ten dollars if I would let her suck my cock.

I did.

And that's how it all began.

CHAPTER TWO

Making $$ At It

The woman who had offered me the money had really stunned me, because as soon as the train had pulled out of Milwaukee, she was sitting next to me. She asked a few leading questions, like how old I was, and I told her eighteen, which she didn't believe. She thought I could maybe pass for seventeen if I brushed my hair back a different way, and when her hand touched my sandy hair, I tingled. "You're really a sharp little kid," she said with a wink.

"You're very pretty," I replied. What I liked about her was the fact that she was about the same age as Liz, but she didn't come on like Liz, there was no sickness in back of her eyes, no pretentions. She wanted me and it was quite clear; she wasn't ashamed about asking, and I wasn't ashamed about agreeing. She came right out and asked if I'd ever had a blow job from a woman before and I told her yes, as a matter of fact, about nine hours ago.

Then I broke down and told her the whole sick story, how Liz had screamed her own son's name, thinking, at least for that moment in her ecstasy, that I was Kent. She really had wanted to make love to her own son all these years, and now that he had a best friend (and one that she probably guessed he had sex with) it was easy to transfer the sexual interest to the friend.

I understood and yet I didn't because I was still very shook up. But she helped calm me by telling me a little about herself, and I was amazed. I learned a lesson from her, although it took years for me to fully come into control of it; I learned to keep my head together under any kind of stress. It is a good thing for a hustler to learn, and it is a requisite if you're to act as a madam, for you have a number of boys in your stud service and you are responsible for their welfare—thus, keeping a cool head under stress is a must.

But that would sink in later. Right then I was fascinated not only by her beauty, but by the fact that she was married to a very wealthy banker in Milwaukee, and traveled to Chicago often to do some "shopping." Which meant finding young boys. She admitted openly that young boys, teenagers, were her passion, that they always had been since she was fifteen and was attacked by a man in his sixties. Ever since that time men scared her, and the gentleness of young boys is what attracted her. They posed no threat, they did not frighten her. She had her husband believing she was slightly frigid, letting him lay her once a month or so, but she knew he had girls on the side, and she was happy for him. But she knew he would never be able to understand her need to suck teenage cock, so she went out of town to do it, to spare him the embarrassment should she ever be caught. "And what do I find, not *in* Chicago, mind you, but on the way *to* Chicago, but you!"

I flashed her my biggest smile.

That's when she offered me the ten bucks. "I'll go to the ladies' room and you follow along the hall and I'll let you in after you tap once."

She started to get up, but another woman beat her to it, so she sat back down next to me. By that time I was already getting hard, and my pants were filling out. She looked down and saw the bulge in my crotch and slipped her hand down there and licked her lips. "God, but you feel big!" she gasped.

"I am."

"Oh, this has got to be my lucky day!"

Mine too, I hoped.

We waited for the other woman to get out of the john, but she seemed to be taking forever. "Come on and pee,

44

damnit!" my new friend kept saying, which made me laugh.

Finally the woman emerged from the small bathroom, and my friend, whose name I didn't even know, went in. Then I got up, holding my jacket in front of me so no one could see what was happening in my pants, and walked down the aisle to the end of the car and tapped lightly on the bathroom door. In I went in.

She sat on the toilet, fully dressed, while I leaned against the locked door. She had my zipper down in a second and opened the buckle on my belt with one hand. I was amazed at how adept she was, how fast. She knew her stuff.

"Holy Jesus," she said when she pulled my half-hard cock out of my undershorts. She stared at it in amazement and then looked up at me and said, "I just got the best bargain of the year. You could be making money with this kind of equipment!" Then she stared at it again as she pulled my pants down to my knees with her other hand, and then brought it up to cup my balls.

"Oh, please suck it," I said, feeling all the hostility and pain I had been feeling that awful morning turning into lust. I wanted to come more than anything in the world.

"Oh, Tracy, darling, your balls," she moaned, and started licking them. (I had already started having women call me Tracy—when she had asked my name, I didn't want to tell her the truth, and yet I couldn't think up anything other than Fred or Hank, and they sounded dumb, so I told her Tracy, my middle name, which no one had ever called me before. I would remain Tracy Saxon all the way to California.)

I went nuts. I never knew—and I knew a hell of a lot of things by this time—that a person could take all of a guy's testicles into their mouth. And I had pretty big balls! She sucked one in, and then the other, and then, dipping her head real low as I spread my legs as far as I could with my underwear and pants being jumbled around my ankles, she sucked both of my nuts into her mouth and wrapped her tongue over them. I couldn't stand it and I grabbed my cock in my hand to start beating off because I wanted to come so badly, but she slapped

45

my hand and stopped me. She wanted her ten bucks' worth!

And she got it, believe me—today I would charge at least fifty bucks for the same treatment.

She sucked my balls just as though she were sucking a cock, up and down, pulling them in and out of her mouth, tickling my asshole with her fingers, playing lightly with my cock, which was looming out over her head.

Then she licked my thighs and nestled her head into my crotch, letting her dark, shining hair entwine around my cock, kissing the shaft, the tip, but not quite taking it in her mouth, no matter how much I pleaded and begged. Finally, with my pubic hair, which still wasn't very thick, covered with her saliva, she grasped the base of my dick and held it out at a ninety-degree angle to my body.

"Please . . ." I couldn't stand it!

She took it, all at once. Her lips fitted around the tip and continued down as far as they could, the head of my dick resting down in her throat for a minute while she closed her eyes and stopped moving her fingers over my wet balls.

"Oh, it feels so good," I moaned, rocking my hips.

"Mmmmmmmm," she moaned back, agreeing, I guess. Then she started moving back and forth, working her hand and lips and tongue until I thought I would crack up.

"I'm commmmming . . ."

"No," she said, pulling her lips from my cock, "not yet, not yet, please, just let me taste it awhile longer." And she went back to it and started sucking lightly, almost tickling the underside of the head, which I loved. I closed my eyes and listened to the rumble of the train and then I realized we were slowing down.

"We're stopping," I said, and that was enough to get her to bring me off. She slammed her face down so hard on my dick, I didn't know how the hell she didn't gag! (I know now; I'm an expert.)

I heard the conductor shout, "Kenosha. Kenosha, next stop. Keeeeenosha!"

And with that I cringed, pushed my cold naked ass off the metal door of the little bathroom, and shot off into her mouth. She tried to swallow all of it, but I guess there was so much she choked a little, and a dribble of cum ran down to her black dress. But she didn't seem to mind, because she moaned and purred all the time she was down there, even as my cock began to soften in her mouth as the train came to a stop.

When I heard people talking and moving around in the aisle, I said, "Shouldn't we go back to our seats now?"

She looked up and finally let my cock fall from her mouth. "Yes, now's the best time."

So I hitched up my pants, only after she again kissed my dick, and when she had wiped the dribble of cum from the front of her dress, we opened the door to the bathroom and drifted into the clump of people lining the aisle, getting on and off at the Kenosha depot.

Once the train pulled out again, we started talking. She asked what I planned to do after I changed trains in Chicago and continued on to Kansas City. Did I have money to exist in Kansas City?

"I have the ten dollars you gave me," I said, feeling it tucked in the pocket of my pants.

"That's it?" she asked in surprise.

"Yes."

"Kid, how do you expect to live?"

I shrugged. "I guess I'll get a job, I don't know."

She paused a minute and then said, "Look, I wouldn't advise this to just anyone, but I think maybe you can handle it, seeing what you've been through."

I was puzzled. I didn't know what she meant.

"What I'm saying is you don't need a job—you *are* a job! Lots of women like me will pay lots of money to get a taste of what's in your pants. Find one who'll give you a place to live, clothes on your back, food on the table, an education. You've got more than enough to pay for it."

I still was perplexed. *A guy's cock can't do all that!* I didn't know what to say, but she could read my mind.

"Look, it's not just that you're *hung*."

I smiled. It was the first time I had ever heard the word. I liked it.

"It's more than that," she continued. "It's your face

47

and your body too, and a kind of sparkle in your eyes. You're a beautiful boy, you know that? Just little-boyish enough to be appealing to older gals like me, and enough of a stud to sock it to the best of us."

"I . . . I don't know what I want to do," I said.

"Come on, honey, there's a brain in there somewhere," she said, playfully knocking at my head.

"Well, I sure like to read."

"Do you?"

I nodded enthusiastically. I loved reading. Math, you could shove it. Sports, nah. Geography, bullshit. Reading, literature, fantastic! So she reached in her bag and pulled out a book and handed it to me.

"For me?" I asked.

"Yes, for you. Unless you've already read it."

I looked at the title. *Tender Is The Night*, by F. Scott Fitzgerald. "I've read some of his short stories, but never a novel. Thank you!" I really appreciated it. No one had ever given me a book before, ever. I clutched it to my chest with a big smile on my face.

Then she reached in her bag again and pulled out a pen. "Give it back a second," she said, "and I'll write something in it."

I handed it to her and said, "Sure, great," and she wrote something, very quickly, with a fast sweep of her hand. Then when she handed it back to me and I didn't look to see what she had written, she asked, "You're not going to look at it now?"

"No, I'd rather wait till . . . well, till when we've parted."

"I understand," she said, and then kissed me on the cheek. "I do hope you'll like it."

"I will, oh, I'm sure I will." I looked out the window of the train and the frozen husks of corn were standing up from the snow in the fields. It was a beautiful, crisp winter day, a perfect day on which to begin a new life.

"Listen," she said after a few minutes, "would you like to make another ten bucks?"

I turned to her. "How?" I asked naively.

"Can you come again? We can fuck standing up in the bathroom."

I grinned my most shit-eatingest little-boy grin and then we went back to the bathroom. And stayed there till the train pulled into Chicago.

Chicago, Illinois. Quite a city, I was to find out, and it is funny, almost, that I should end up back here, as I am writing this journal. I would feel a myriad emotions about Chicago in my life and career. I would be enchanted by it, then hate it. Then, I would come to love it, come to call it home. And I would grow restless when I would hear of the good life and the money a boy could make in California. I would leave. And I would return.

You see, when we got off the train and as I held my gift book in one hand and my little suitcase in the other, the beautiful woman who had just finished emptying my cock for the second time that day told me, "Cash in the rest of that ticket and get the money. Find yourself a place to stay for the night. If you go on to Kansas City, you won't find anything for twenty dollars, at least you won't find anything to hold you very long. There are people with money here in Chicago, people who will set you up fine, even though you're underage. Listen, take my advice, call Helen, here's her card." She reached into her bag again and finally found a calling card printed, simply: HELEN FEderal 8-1636.

I took the card, stuffed it in the pocket with the two rolled tens, and waved goodbye. I watched her as she walked away, almost sorry that we had to part. I found myself wishing she were able to be satisfied with only one boy and that that boy could be me. An apartment all my own in Chicago . . .

I was dreaming, but it's nice to dream when you have little else.

So I took her advice. I cashed in the rest of my ticket and decided to try my luck in Chicago, but I wasn't going to call Helen Whoevershewas. I wanted to strike out on my own. With my luck she would turn out to be another Liz Reynauld, and then where would I be?

I put a quarter in a slot for a locker in the train station and put my suitcase in it. Then I set the book inside, but I remembered I hadn't yet looked at what she had written. So I opened it and read:

To Tracy—
   who made me feel, at least
   for a moment, I was in Paris—

                Eleanor

So her name was Eleanor and she had been my first trick.

I hope there were many others who were able to give her Paris.

I had been to Chicago a few times before, but never on my own. And to be there alone, in the middle of winter, with the night coming on, can be frightening. I don't know why I didn't take a hotel room or why I didn't call the number Eleanor had given me. I guess I was afraid a hotel would ask my age and turn me away, and that Helen would lock me up permanently—I had visions of this mad woman keeping young boys in cells and throwing them raw meat every three days. I was really a mess.

I tried to have fun that afternoon, trying my damnedest to feel as free as I was supposed to feel, trying to lose myself in the midst of the tall buildings and the crowds. But the buildings seemed just a bit taller than Milwaukee's and the crowds were not so plentiful because of the snow. To this day, I would not recommend January in Chicago to anyone. Even I get out of the city in January now.

But, being a broke teenager then, there was little way to get out. I spent some of my money on food, and then, when I got cold again, I went to a movie in the Loop. I have no idea what it was about, only that it starred Elizabeth Taylor, but even her beauty was not enough to keep me awake. An usher woke me three times, and asked me to leave on the fourth. Just as I was getting up to follow his orders and his flashlight, a man's voice said, "He's with me. I won't let him fall asleep again."

What the hell? I turned to see a handsome man sitting one seat away from me, looking at the usher with a very matter-of-fact expression on his face. It worked. The usher (a kid not much older than myself) nodded and walked away. I turned to the man and thanked him and then added, "But why did you say that?"

" 'Cause I didn't want to see you get tossed in the cold," he replied. He had a soothing voice, and he talked rather loudly because the theater was nearly empty, and we were in the back row. Why the usher didn't let me sleep is beyond me—was I snoring? I never asked. I don't think I've ever snored in my life, to tell the truth.

Somehow the man knew I had nowhere to go. I think he sensed it—there are people who can "feel" runaways, and many of them, unfortunately, are vice cops, but that too I would find out much later. For now I had a man sitting a seat away from me in a dark movie theater, asking me if I wanted to go home with him. I did, I mean I did want to go home with him, because I needed a place to stay, but I didn't want to do anything more than that. There had been a certain safety in having sex with Kent, and even when Frank, the chauffeur, was involved, it seemed rather natural. But now, for some odd reason, the situation seemed dangerous. My first instinct was to go with him, and if I had followed it I would have been in a warm bed that night, could have had a good sleep, a fine breakfast, and, most likely, a pocketful of money by morning. *If* I had had my shit together, which I did not. So I politely refused him. He offered me money, just how much I don't remember, but I refused that too. I was scared. Finally he begged me, saying I could have anything I wanted.

"I said no, so please leave me alone," I said, and moved to another seat, across the aisle.

He came and sat next to me.

I moved again, and again he followed.

I was beginning to sweat. "Come on, baby, I'll set you up real good, I know you're fresh off the bus!" I heard those words and tears started welling up in my eyes and I clenched my fists. Then he said, "Honey, with the ass on you, I can get a hundred dollars a night on you easy."

"Fuck yourself!" I said, jumping up and all but running up the aisle. But—dummy that I was—I didn't leave the theater; I went to the men's room. I got in there and looked in the mirror and was surprised to see how tired I looked, how red my eyes were. I splashed some water on my face, cool water, and then patted it dry. And then, just as I pulled my cock out of my pants to take a leak, he walked in.

"Nobody tells Joey DeFranco to *fuck himself*." It was too unreal, right out of an Al Capone Chicago gangster movie. *Joey DeFranco*. I thought he was kidding at first, so I smiled, standing there at the urinal like an idiot with my cock in my hands. I think I was still smiling when he hit me.

All I remember is him coming at me, his arm raised, and me with that stupid grin and a violent effort to stuff my dick back in my pants. It was the first time I had ever encountered physical violence in my life, and it wouldn't be the last. But I wasn't ready for it. I can still feel my entire body flying across the sterile-smelling room, my head hitting the metal of the toilet stalls, and his voice booming, "PUNK! FUCKING LITTLE PUNK!"

(Three years ago, while I was vacationing with a female client in Venice, I received a clipping from the *Chicago Daily News* which showed police fishing something big and green out of the Chicago River. Joey DeFranco had met his maker in typical Chicago gangland fashion—choked, shot, wrapped in a garbage bag with a chunk of cement, and nicely deposited in the river of sewage. It was a fitting end for a monster who had turned more teenage boys into heroin addicts than any pusher in the Midwest. Apparently others hated him as much as I did. I thank God I received only a beating from him that night in the men's room of the theater; what would have become of me had I said yes and gone home with him?)

I came to and found myself in the arms of the usher who had shined the flashlight in my face. I was bleeding from a small wound in my forehead—there is still a tiny scar there today—and I thought my arm was broken, but it was merely sprained. But it hurt, inside and out, and as the boy dabbed wadded-up paper towels on my head, I wished I had stayed at the Reynauld house and learned how to deal with Liz. Could it have been any worse than where I had ended up that night?

"Do you want me to call the police?" the usher asked. "I'm supposed to, you know."

I must have looked mighty scared because I didn't need to answer him.

"Okay, I understand," he said, and then gently patted my head, trying to stop the bleeding. I sensed immediately that he was gay. I don't know what it was, the way he held me? The way he looked at me? The fact that he had gone to all that trouble to wake me up each time when I wasn't bothering anyone? And when I say I knew he was gay, I don't mean I realized he was sexually attracted to me—I'll never know if he was or not. I mean to say that I felt that he liked boys as opposed to girls, because there was a gentleness about him which was completely different from all the boys I had gone to school with. I would see that gentleness repeated in the makeup of many of the boys who would later work for me.

He took me to a little "manager's office," which consisted of a table and two chairs and a couple of reels of film. They had a first aid kit in there and he put a big bandage on my forehead, which looked silly, but it did the trick. I didn't require stitches and I was glad of that. He was very sweet and told me that he really had thought I was with the guy who had taken a whack at me; otherwise, he said, he would have warned me about him. Yes, he too knew Joey DeFranco. I would soon find that most of Chicago knew Joey DeFranco.

"I'm off work in half an hour," the boy said. "Would you like to go home with me?"

Again, I was scared, the same feeling I had felt when Joey DeFranco had approached me. Kent ran through my mind and I couldn't see this kid, even though he was very good-looking and had cared for me and had been good enough not to call the police on me, taking Kent's place in bed. "No, I have to go to my aunt Helen's."

He looked sincerely disappointed.

"I'm sorry," I said, and he nodded. Then I pulled out the little card with Helen's number on it, the calling card

Eleanor had given me, and the usher let me use the phone in the office.

After three rings, a woman's voice said, merely, "Yes?"

"Um . . . Helen?"

"One moment. Can I ask who's calling?"

"Gra . . . I mean, Tracy. Tracy Saxon. I don't think she knows who—" I heard a click and realized someone had evidently come on the line with us. Then another click, and I knew the woman who had answered had hung up.

"You don't think who knows who?" the woman's booming voice asked.

"Me. I don't think Helen knows me."

"I'm Helen. Who is this?"

"Tracy Saxon."

"Eleanor!"

"Yes . . . yes, then Eleanor told you I might be calling." I was trembling, but I was damn glad she knew who I was.

"Tracy, honey, anyone Eleanor sends me is royalty, believe me! Where are you, baby?"

I told her the name of the theater. "On State Street," the usher whispered. I added, "On State Street."

"Listen, you hop in a cab and you tell 'em you want to go to this address on North LaSalle Street. I'll be watching out the window."

"Thank you," I said, hanging up. I picked up a pencil from the desk and wrote the address on the back of the calling card and then looked up at the usher, surprised to see a hurt expression on his face.

"You lied to me," he said.

"What?"

"She's not your aunt. You don't even know her."

What could I say? I felt bad enough already, and if I stuck around any longer I was sure things would get worse. I thanked the usher again, but he didn't acknowledge it, and walked out into the freezing night air.

Suddenly my head began to ache terribly, and when I finally got into a cab—the first taxi I had been in in my life—I mumbled the address and put my head back, feeling dizzy.

"You got the money to pay, kid?" the cabbie asked.

"My aunt will pay you when we get there."

He looked at the address he had just written on his pad. He nodded and snuffed, "Yeah, I guess with an address like this, she'll have have the coins."

Well, I thought as we rode along, at least Helen lives in a nice place.

Another understatement. A palace you could have called it. It's really too bad there are no whorehouses left like hers any longer. Helen's place has since become a high-rise development named Carl Sandburg Village. But in its day it was one of the best, one of the most beautiful, and certainly one of the most popular.

And it's where I got my basic training, so to speak.

Helen was a lesbian who tended toward the butch, but she didn't come on too strong because she had the shape of a Mama Cass or Totie Fields. She was an amazing woman, warm and understanding, but firm and demanding. Her girls (and her boys, of which I became one) were the finest the city had to offer. She was fair to them, gave them one night off every week, served them the best of food, kept them in the best of shape by making them visit a superb doctor every three weeks, and insisted on cleanliness of body and spirit. That is to say the attitude of everyone who worked in her place was one of good feeling and high spirits—no bitch fights between the girls, no cat fights, no drunken johns throwing furniture out the windows, no one being allowed special favors or outlandish credit. It was a well-run house, and I was happy there—until I grew restless.

Let me go back a bit. Helen met me at the cab with one of the girls, a beautiful black girl called Lacey, and they helped me into the house. While I sat in a red velvet chair in front of a warm fire, they sponged my wound and rubbed something into the other little cuts I'd received. Then Lacey appeared from the kitchen (Miss Pearl, Lacey's real great aunt, was the cook, a big old southern mammy, and she had made a huge pot of soup that evening, which, thankfully, the customers had not finished off) with a bowl of steaming bean soup and homemade bread.

I ate, told Helen the story of my life, saw her wince at the mention of Joey DeFranco, saw her smile when I told her I wanted to retrieve my copy of *Tender Is The Night*, and saw her look me up and down with obvious interest.

Finally, when I had finished, she asked, quite simply, "You want to work for me? I'll get your identification changed so you'll be nineteen. You'll get half of what the customers pay for your services, and what you don't already know, I'll teach you. How long is your cock?"

I blinked. "Wh . . . what?"

"My ladies want to know sometimes. Jerry, his is seven inches. Paul's got an average six, but it's nice and thick. I've been needing a third boy for a long time now, but I just haven't found the right one. I need someone *hung*." There was that word again!

"I don't really know how big it is," I finally said.

She winked. "That's all right, 'cause Eleanor already told me. That's why I was happy to hear you call. I want to help you, Tracy, and in turn, you'll help me. No strings attached, you can walk out the door anytime you like."

It sounded wonderful.

I learned about life in a whorehouse. A house of prostitution. A cathouse. A brothel. Whatever you call it, it's the same thing—home to the people who live and work there. A few of Helen's girls lived elsewhere, either in apartments of their own, with their boyfriends, or, in two cases, with their husbands (that sure as hell surprised me). Paul lived there, and we got to be good friends and spent a lot of time together. Jerry was going to college on his money, and he "lived" in a dormitory at Northwestern University in Evanston, although I can't remember one night he was ever in his bed in the dorm. I had a room overlooking LaSalle Street, on the third floor of the house, and I remember sitting in the window for hours during the day, especially in March and April when it rained a lot, thinking, dreaming of California. . . .

56

Paul and I had a dream, and we were constantly telling Helen about it, and she laughed and told us we'd end up "fifty-cent hustlers on Hollywood and Vine," when we told her we planned on being movie stars. Or, at the very least, kept boys of famous movie stars. Oh, how I wanted Elizabeth Taylor to own me!

So I had set a goal, and I had to work toward it, and I knew it would take time and money, and in the business I was in it took time to earn money. At first I made very little because I was just learning. But by the time May rolled around I was doing very well, enjoying the popularity of being Helen's "best boy," and stashing my money away for my magic journey to California.

I liked being a prostitute. It was a wonderfully secure job, it was exciting, especially for a young horny kid like me, it was interesting because I met all kinds of women from all walks of life, and it was educational—people were damned interesting! Besides that, Helen was a smart woman, and her library was filled to the ceiling with books, and I read as many of them as I could. I remember how desperately she had wanted me to read all of Gertrude Stein, and how difficult I found it at first, and the many times I would sit on my bed reading a certain passage again and again and again, until the bell rang, signaling me someone was on their way up, and I'd hide the book under the bed, drop my pants, and stretch out on the bed with my cock in my hand and a big smile on my face. That's the way I greeted the ladies I serviced, and they all seemed to love it.

Helen had let me relax for the first few days I was there, and with the bump on my head and all I don't suppose I was the most attractive platter to serve a customer. So I roamed the house and got the feel of the place, made friends with big fat Miss Pearl, whose pecan pies I can remember to this day, and took long walks in the snow with Paul, who seemed to be filling, in some ways, the void Kent's friendship had left in my life. I wrote a thank-you note to Eleanor and asked Helen to send it to her, telling her I had loved the book (true) and was grateful to her for giving me Helen's phone number.

But my strength was soon returning and with it came

the raging hard-on I usually carried around in my pants. I was hot and eager to start work—beating off just wouldn't do any longer.

So Helen asked me if I cared to perform for her, with Lacey, so she could study my technique and see where I needed some improvements. I agreed, nearly foaming at the mouth; I had wanted to make it with Lacey ever since I had first seen her. Helen told me we would get together the next morning, and I should not beat off that night or before breakfast because "a tired stud is no stud at all." I have never forgotten those words, and they are the first words I tell any new boy who works for me.

Women have an easier time being prostitutes than men do; they have nothing to "get up." If they are sexually turned off to the man they're with, chances are the man won't know it. The girl may hate his guts, find him revolting, and yet she stands a good chance of gaining a tip if she makes one phony "ooooh" or "ahhhh" or wraps her legs around his behind, pretending she is adoring the fact that his cock is inside her. The trick can be making passionate love to her and she can be thinking about the weather or Prince Charles or what to buy her mother for Christmas. The trick will never know.

But a stud is stuck with something which will give his feelings away at the slightest glance—a penis. If it is big and hard, the customer knows he or she is satisfying you and that he or she is getting their money's worth. If you go limp, you may as well go out the window. A guy's cock is sort of a barometer of sex, and if you're going to make a living at being a stud, you'd better learn to keep it up.

I've been lucky—seems I'm naturally horny, which means I can get an erection at the snap of a finger. But for some goddamned reason, the morning when I was to show Helen just what a great little fucker I was, my peter petered out on me. I couldn't get it up to fuck Lacey for love nor money (not that she was offering either) and Helen thought perhaps it was the fact that I still hadn't recovered from my little meeting with Joey DeFranco. I told her I felt fine. She asked me if I

58

had gone ahead and beat off in the night, if I had had a wet dream. Nope, not that I knew of. Fact was, I had had a nightmare. Did I want to try another girl instead of Lacey? No, I didn't think that would do any good. Did I want a boy? No, not unless his name was Kent, but I wouldn't have given Lacey up for him. So what was my problem? I'd never had trouble getting an erection in my life!

Lacey tried everything, jerking me up and down, turning me on my stomach and licking my ass gently, first each buttock, then between them, and finally spreading them with her hands, sticking her tongue into my rectum just a little. It felt sensational, but my dick just hung there like Slotkowski Polish sausage in the meat market—dead. Lacey sucked on it, licked my balls, let me play with her beautiful breasts, let me spread her vagina and run my tongue up and down, tickling her clit with both my tongue and fingers, but still, where it counted most, I was a failure.

Helen got up and left.

"Sorry, baby, but it happens," Lacey said, lighting a cigarette. "Just last night I had this john, been coming to me three years now, three whole years!" I could hardly believe she had been a whore for three years—she looked as though she couldn't have been older than eighteen. "Last night he conks out, just like that, pffffffft!"

I giggled. She put her finger in her lips, filled her mouth with air, and made a loud popping sound when she released her finger. "So what did you do?" I asked.

"Played Scrabble."

I fell back onto the bed in a fit of laughter. "Did that get him to get it up for you?"

"No, baby, but it sure as hell made him happy," she said, sitting there in the little chair in the corner of the room, pulling her nightie over her bare brown shoulders.

"Why?"

" 'Cause he *won!*"

And then we both doubled over in laughter. The poor guy comes to the best and most expensive whorehouse in the city of Chicago and ends up winning a game of

Scrabble. "I don't believe it," I cried, laughing till tears filled my eyes. "It's too silly!"

"I know," Lacey laughed, "and it cost the poor bastard a hundred smackeroos!"

"Oh, Christ!" I kicked my feet into the air, feeling impish and wild and crazy all of a sudden. I also happened to realize that my cock was standing out in front of my body.

"Oooooooh, baby," Lacey said, noticing the same thing I did, at the very same time. She stood up and dropped her little nightie to the floor. "Tracy, honey, all you needed was a little loosening up, you was all tight inside!"

And before Helen could make it up the steps (Lacey had pressed the buzzer next to the bed before jumping in with me) we were going at it like dogs in heat.

Helen stood in the door, watching us bouncing on the bed, changing positions, my head pounding from holding back an orgasm for so long, fucking Lacey upside down, sideways, half on the bed, half on the floor, on the chair, standing up, just about everything short of swinging from the chandelier, which we would have done if we could have been sure it would support us. When I finally came, I pulled out, at Lacey's pleas, and shot the rest of my big load all over her face.

"Baby," she moaned, licking the sperm from around her lovely lips, "you're good."

"But I wonder how I'd do at Scrabble?" I replied, and we both fell to the bed in laughter again.

Helen finally gave her seal of approval and walked away, ready to turn me loose on her customers. I guess I knew enough to satisfy most of them, and what I didn't know I'd learn, or I'd improvise. Like any job, the longer you work at it the better at it you become—if you like it.

And I loved what I was doing.

I didn't make a hell of a lot of money right off the bat because, I found out, Helen didn't have a lot of women customers. Most houses are frequented by men since women are usually the sole residents and workers. Some houses keep a few boys for the ladies who wish to pay for their services, although most stud services are just

60

that—services which operate from a switchboard arrangement. The woman calls, she tells me who she wants or the kind of boy she wants if she doesn't know one in particular, what he is to do, how long he is to do it, then I set a price and she either agrees, disagrees, or haggles (I usually win because my boys are the *best*), and finally she tells me where to send him. That's the kind of house I run today, which is not a house at all, in the real sense of the word. Most houses today are apartments and they are filled with girls, and girls only.

Lesbians often visit all girl whorehouses because a great number of hookers are dykes themselves and they sometimes welcome the chance to make money while at the same time really getting it off making love with someone of their own sex. Madams often like to watch the girls perform, since most madams are bisexual, and sometimes they even join in with their girls in a little roll in the hay. I know a madam of a big house in Miami who won't give the girls their money unless they spread their legs for her and allow her to slip the rolled bills into their pussies. She's a gas, honestly—when you call there, chances are she has the phone in one hand and a pretty young coed's tit in the other. There are all kinds. But Xaviera Hollander, the best of them all, has told you about them, so why repeat it here? But let me tell you about male madams, and that's another story completely. . . .

Helen first started explaining it to me when I worked for her that spring. She called me into the library one afternoon and closed the door. "Tracy, you're becoming my most popular boy."

"Thank you," I said. I wondered if it was because of the size of my cock or because I looked so young and gorgeous. Either way, it was great vanity and quite an ego trip, so I didn't ask, figuring I'd get a yes on both accounts.

"I want to ask you something, and I want you to be perfectly frank with me. See, once in a while I get a few guys in here and they decide, maybe after they've had one of the girls, that they wanna try a boy. Or sometimes one of the women customers, she tells me

61

she has a friend, a guy who's gay, and would any of my boys . . . ?" She threw her hands into the air.

"I understand what you're saying. Susan told me only last night that she wished her husband, who's bisexual, could take a go at me."

"She did, huh?" Helen asked, rubbing her chin. "Yeah, well, I don't like it when customers start arranging things themselves."

I learned another lesson right there—keep your mouth shut. If you do, you'll last longer and get bigger tips.

"Tracy, when I get a guy in here, and I only take guys on special reference, you understand, well . . . when I take a guy in here, I charge him a good fee because he's getting something out of the ordinary."

I was confused. "You mean a guy who wants one of us boys, right?"

"Right. Well, I like to give him the most for his money, and since Paul isn't into that scene at all, I give them all to Jerry. I was wondering if you might . . ."

"No."

"No? You made up your mind so fast? You scared?"

"No, that's not it. I just would rather not, at least not now. Maybe in another month or two."

She gave me an understanding look. "You still hurting from the DeFranco thing, right?"

I nodded.

"He'll rot in hell, mark my words," she said, almost spitting. "On my mother's grave, he'll fucking rot in hell." She got up and pulled a book off the shelf and suggested I read it. I don't remember the title, but I know it had something to do with homosexuality. "It might help," she said.

On the way out, I stopped her and asked, "Helen, do they have houses just for boys?"

"You mean exclusively for homosexuals?"

"Yes."

"Sure, but not many. Too many hustlers on the streets, they're too easy to find. That's why I was asking you— seems some of the better class of people don't want to risk picking up kids out of the alleys, even if they've put lights in them now."

I smiled at that.

"See, Tracy," she said, putting her stubby arm on my shoulder, "running a house isn't easy. It takes a firm fist, an eye for cops and raids, a brain for keeping books, for remembering which guy gets which girl, which guy likes Jeannie to give him a bubble bath, which guy demands tea to be served right after he comes, which guy wants French ticklers. I know a lot of madams, and some of them have the right kind of heads for this work, and I'm one of them. But I've never met a male homosexual who could do it. Something too flighty about them. Gay houses just don't last."

I have come to learn that what she said that day has some truth in it, although it is largely a generalization. I can dispute the theory by telling you about a gay house in New Orleans which is run by two of the silliest, simpiest queens you'd ever want to (or never want to) meet. You'd swear they can't fart and wave at the same time, but I mean it, they have one of the best houses going—and I mean *house*, two floors of southern-plantation charm and charming southern boys.

But Helen was right in a lot of ways; gay houses usually are run by the wrong people, and thus they close down. Even the stud services come and go like the wind. One will open up and the code will be dropped into underground—or are they now more *above*ground?—newspapers like the *Advocate*, the *L.A. Free Press*, *Screw*, the *Berkeley Barb*, *San Francisco Ball*, and many others. If they catch on, and they usually do at first, the current trend being listing them as "private massage—choose from a list of hunky masseurs," the code spreads to the big-time rags, the *New York Times*, the *Chicago Tribune*, the *Washington Post*, the *San Francisco Chronicle*, the *Los Angeles Times*, the *St. Louis Post-Dispatch*, and more. But they're loosely connected organizations which usually grow past any hope of management—that's why I keep only a certain number of boys, no more, no less, and survive—and they soon fall apart, and the kids who were with them take to the streets once again.

I don't think Helen meant that all homosexuals are flighty. But it takes a hustler with a good head on his shoulders to run a house; that is, it takes a good hustler to bridge the step from just-plain-hustler to madam.

I've done it, but I'm one of the few.

In an all-boy house, when it's in one residence as the New Orleans place is, you have to be careful of something else: A man will sometimes resent it if he finds out the trick his beautiful little boy had just an hour before him was a woman. Many (most?) homosexuals paying for a hunky nineteen-year-old cock don't like to know that that hunky dick has recently been inside a cunt! And the same goes with a woman customer. If she's shelling out good money for a stud, she sometimes doesn't like to find out his nine inches are more often than not up the asshole of a forty-year-old man. You can lose business if your customers are not kept satisfied, thus you must make sure, if you're working out of one place, that the appointments are set up at the right times, that they don't conflict, and if you don't set up appointments, for God's sake at least arrange a way to get the guy out before the woman goes in, or vice versa. It can get rather confusing, as you can see. That's why I prefer a service—I'll send the boys to you, or I'll arrange a room somewhere for you. There's less chance of getting busted that way, too, and I've had that happen.

Which is a later story.

Right now, life at Helen's was a tremendous experience. I learned to participate in three-ways, when a woman wanted one, and Paul and I usually shared her. He fucked her in the pussy while she sucked me off (seems the customers wanted the bigger cocks in their mouths and the smaller ones up their cunts), or I jerked off between her breasts as she licked my asshole, while Paul fucked her, kneeling between her legs. One time, with a wild woman with flaming red hair, I put my dick up her pussy, standing up, while Paul slid his up her behind, and I was amazed that I could feel his cock rubbing against mine inside her! She evidently liked it too—she tipped us twenty-five dollars each.

But Paul and I had our dream, and as the days in Chicago grew warmer; so did our desire to get to the land of sunshine and orange juice.

We had some money saved, and we planned on leaving the morning of June fourth. That day has always held special meaning for me, good and bad. It is, first of all, my birthday—yes, I'm a crazy Gemini. It's the day one of my boys graduated from college, which pleased me because he, like Jerry at Helen's house, had put himself through school entirely on the money he made hustling, and I got him good fees. It was Flo's birthday, too, (you'll read about her later) my "sugar mama" who fell off a goddamned Alp in Auntie Mame style (you'll read about *that* later) and died on me. And I'll never forget, as long as I live, that June fourth was the day of the California primary in 1968, a jubilant night for me because someone I loved and believed in had accomplished something tremendous—and then the crashing end came and Bobby Kennedy was gone.

But yes, June fourth was the day we were to leave for Los Angeles, and Helen muttered all week, wondering where she could ever find replacements, wondering how she would ever survive without her "two lovelies," as she called us. (She survived fine; within a week she had two new guys in the house and the customers were lining up down the block. Miss Pearl wrote me that herself!)

Paul and I got our airline tickets, which took a good chunk of our cash, but we figured we would find a house as fine as or finer than Helen's as soon as we stepped off the plane into the sunshine, so we weren't worried. We bought some new clothes and gave some of our older things away to kids in Old Town, which was right around the corner from the house. We bought Helen a going-away present (although we were the ones going), a leather-bound copy of all of Gertrude Stein's writing, which was very expensive, but how could I ever repay her for what she had done for me?

And before I left I wanted to do two things, and I did them. I asked Helen if she would break the rules and give me Eleanor's telephone number. I wanted so to thank her. I had begun to wonder why she never came to Chicago, to the house, or if she did why she never asked to see me. Helen explained that her husband had suffered a heart attack and she was staying near him during the winter because he was quite weak and needed someone at his side.

Well, Helen didn't give me the number, but she called Eleanor in Milwaukee herself, and after chatting a few minutes, she let me get on the line. "Hi, remember me?" I asked.

"Remember you? I'll never forget you, Paris!" she said.

"I . . . I just wanted to tell you I did what you suggested, I stayed in Chicago till I got on my feet, and now I'm off to California."

"Oh, Tracy, that's wonderful!"

"I really wish you the best, and thanks again," I said.

"God bless you, Tracy," she said.

Miss Pearl wrote me later (she wrote regularly until she died in 1971) that Eleanor's husband had finally passed away, and Eleanor seemed to disappear from sight. I once tried looking her up when I was in Milwaukee, but could find no trace of her. (Eleanor, wherever you are, if you're reading this book, hi!)

The other thing I wanted to do before I left Chicago was talk to Kent. I had been corresponding with him ever since I walked out of the Reynauld mansion that cold winter morning, listening to his woes of academy life (he hated the place) while he heard about my ever-growing love of what I was doing and where I was doing it. The only thing we never really mentioned was his mother, at least not in detail. He would write, "Mother is sorry you left, but wishes you well." And I would respond, "Give my best to your mother," or some such shit. I always guessed that he knew what had happened—he knew it wasn't like me to pick up one morning in the snow and move out, especially the very day after I had seen him off at his new school. I had looked damned content then, if a little sad that I wouldn't be close to him for a few months, but certainly not on the brink of running away from the closest thing I'd ever had to a home.

So I called him. School had finished and I figured he would be at home, since it was early morning, a beautiful morning as I remember it. Connie answered. "Reynauld residence, good morning," she sang.

"May I speak to Kent please?"

"I'm sorry, but I believe he's still sleeping. . . ." Her voice faltered for a moment and then she asked, "Is this Grant?" She sounded excited.

"Yes. Connie? Hi!"

"Hi, oh, hi! Wait, I'll wake Kent, he'll be so thrilled!"

I waited a few moments until I heard him pick up the extension in his room and gasp, "Grant?"

"The one and only!"

"JESUS CHRIST!"

And then we went completely berserk, talking our heads off about anything and everything. He told me my parents were still doing the tent shows and that they had kept in contact with his mother. I didn't ask if they ever inquired about me because I knew they didn't, and, what's more, it didn't matter. I had never really had parents anyway.

But Kent had a mother, and she had to be talked about. I didn't know how to approach the situation because I felt I couldn't come out with it and tell him that his up- standing mother had come into my room and bounced on my dick while shouting his name into the heavens. But, on the other hand, I knew he had been hurt by my sudden picking up and leaving, and I wanted to explain why.

He was the better man of the two. He started it off. "Grant, I figured things out after you left. I mean, it all came into place, why Mother backed the revival thing with your parents, why she sent me away. Frank was drunk one night and told me about her telling you to call her *Liz*. Grant, I would have run away too, and I'm going to."

"What?"

"I'm going off to Europe for the summer, on a tour with a bunch of other kids, and then I'm diving into college as soon as I get back."

I was glad for him, glad that he realized that what had happened had not been my fault, glad he was getting away from his mother, glad too that he would never have to know she was actually in love with him, and not with me, as he thought.

67

"Friends forever," I asked, "even if I become a famous movie star?"

"Friends forever," he said with a laugh, "even if you end up a garbage man!"

"Fuck you, is that the kind of confidence you have in me?"

His voice turned suddenly compassionate and he said, very seriously, "Tracy, it's a big world out there. I guess I don't *know* that through any kind of experience; no Reynauld gets to know the world through experience. But I believe what I read and some of the things I sense. Be careful. And if you ever need me, I'm right here."

Three weeks later, broke, confused, sick of letting guys suck my cock for a lousy few bucks a shot on Selma Avenue in Hollywood, hungry and longing for someone to talk to, I called Kent, remembering his words.

Frank told me he was in Europe and would be back in early September. I had missed his departure by two days.

Sometimes I have the shittiest luck!

CHAPTER THREE

Hollywood—The Bad Times

There's an empty feeling you get deep inside you somewhere when you leave something, someone, or some place, and know you're never coming back to that exact something, someone, or some place again. That's the feeling I had as the big TWA jet lifted off the ground and circled around O'Hare and then nosed its way up through the clouds till we could no longer see ground. Gone was the happy, easy, fun-loving life of a young hustler in a superb whorehouse, gone were Helen, Lacey, Miss Pearl, Jerry, and the others, gone was Chicago.

I didn't say a word for a long time, but Paul finally spoke up. "Tracy, you really think it's going to work out as well as we're hoping?"

"Sure, Paul, sure!" But I think he knew I didn't believe a word I was saying. So I tried changing the subject. "You know, flying in one of these things is even more fantastic than I had hoped." That, too, was a lie— it was just as I had expected it to be.

Even the gaiety of my birthday party at the house the evening before hadn't carried over. I was being hit with a bad case of insecurity, not unlike the way I felt the day I dropped that quarter into the locker slot, shoved my suitcase in, and set out into the snows of Chicago.

This time it would be the sands of California, but who was to assure me it was to be any warmer?

Oh, it was exciting to see the palm trees and the people walking around half naked, suntans, sunglasses, exactly as I had pictured it. As Paul and I rode the bus from Los Angeles International Airport into Hollywood, our spirits picked up. We began to feel once again that we were embarking on a wonderful adventure, and that fortune and happiness lay ahead.

We got a room in a hotel just off Hollywood Boulevard, nothing special, nothing too crummy, a place where we could sleep and, if we had to, trick. We knew it would take some time to get set up in houses or with a good madam who took care of her boys the way Helen did. Of course, we were telling ourselves that we wanted to strike out on our own, that we didn't want to work for anyone, we wanted to hustle for ourselves, but deep down inside we were very, very young and I think each of us realized that the security of a place like Helen's was what we needed.

However, Los Angeles is a big town and I soon found out it is full of handsome boys—most of them ready to drop their pants at the clink of a dime. Sex is different in California from anywhere else in the world; indeed, I honestly believe Hollywood is a hell of a lot more promiscuous than Europe. The sexual standards in California are so radically different from the rest of the country that a hustler used to a good place like Helen's could think he landed in Amsterdam rather than Beverly Hills. Sex is taken for granted in California, and everyone is selling it, cheap, and, if they're not selling it, they're giving it away. If there is a sexual revolution in America today (and there is), it began in California.

Which makes life for a hustler difficult—until you meet the right people, go to the right parties, say and do the right things. I never quite did anything right in California in all the time I stayed there, but I learned a lot—a lot about sex and a lot about people.

The casual atmosphere was the first thing which interested me, the casual atmosphere toward anything at all. People shop in grocery stores as though they were merely out for a walk along Lake Michigan, casually throwing things into the cart now and then. They drive their cars on the freeways like crazy, but when they get to where they are going, they collapse! Everyone is crashing, all the time, lying on the beach, lying by the pool, even telephones are set out on the patios so people don't have to overtax themselves by walking into the house to answer it. Just about everything is taken for granted, earthquakes included.

Sex is taken for granted; it is part of everything in California, part of the way waitresses serve food, part of the way stars are born, part of the way men drive cabs and trim trees. Everybody *fucks* everybody! Paul and I learned that when, after being in Los Angeles only thirty-six hours, we had been invited to three orgies, offered something like six blow jobs apiece, and been cruised by just about every pair of eyes, male and female, which had come upon us.

The place is a sexual Disneyland!

Paul got lucky first. He met a woman in the lobby of the hotel and they went for a walk. He came back two days later with a beautiful tan. I asked him where in the hell he had been. I was beginning to worry. He explained she had a house on the beach and she took him there and they fucked for two days. How much did she pay him? Not much, he said. I think he was so ashamed that the amount was so small that he refused to actually tell me how much he got. I think he did it for the fun of it, because fucking women in their thirties and forties was really his bag. But he knew she wouldn't be coming back for more, and, if by some chance she did, she would never be able to support him.

And how did I do? Well, dreams of stardom began falling quick on the afternoon of the fifth day we were there. I walked down to Hollywood Boulevard and grabbed a fast breakfast at a little restaurant on the corner of Las Palmas Avenue, then walked down the street, past the big newsstand, to Selma Avenue, famous for its hustlers. I had heard many stories of the money to be made by being young and hung and standing on Selma Avenue in Hollywood, and I was eager to see what the place was like. What was it like? Any street. Except at night it was lined with boys, and the cars never stopped circling.

71

During the day it was another story, although you could spot a hustler here and there. I guess most guys took to Griffith Park and to the beaches during the day, and hit Selma as soon as darkness fell. But when I hit Selma, and turned east to walk to the big post office on the corner of Wilcox, I encountered one of the craziest and nearly unbelievable (at least it was then; now I'll believe anything) experiences of my life.

I was walking down the street when I realized a car was traveling alongside me, going as slowly as I was. I glanced over and saw a very ugly man sitting behind the steering wheel of a very expensive automobile. I thought, *oh, no, try your luck somewhere else, fatso*. See, at that time I still had money and somewhat of a hangup about homosexuality.

Well, the guy sped on finally, but he circled the block and drove up to me again, pulling alongside the curb this time. I looked at him and distinctly did not smile. Then I turned and continued.

So did he.

He followed me till I reached the corner where the Hollywood YMCA is, Hudson Street, and just as I was about to cross the street he turned in front of me, nearly running his front tires over my feet. I jumped back to the curb and glared at him. He turned off the ignition and motioned for me to come to the car. I walked over and leaned down.

"I want to ask you a personal question," he said.

"The answer is no," I replied, and started to move away, but he asked me to wait. I looked back in the car and I saw him pull a fat wallet from his pocket and whip out two crisp ten-dollar bills. "No thanks," I said.

"Listen, all I want to do is ask you a question," he insisted.

"Then why are you flashing money in my face?"

"Because I want to buy something from you and I'm wondering if you care to sell what I'm looking for."

"Look, I'm straight," I said.

"That has nothing to do with it. I want to ask you a simple personal question."

72

I was off the track by then. I didn't know what his story was. So I nodded and said, "Ask away."

"Are you wearing underwear?"

I blinked. "Did I hear you right?"

"Yes, I'm afraid you did."

"That *is* a personal question. As a matter of fact, yes, I am."

"Good. Would you consider selling them to me?"

What? This time I was sure I hadn't heard him correctly. "You want to buy my undershorts?"

"Only if they're briefs, no boxers." He held the twenty dollars in his hand.

"Um . . . I . . . well . . ." I stuttered and stammered. Here was a guy offering to buy the shorts I was wearing! Why? How? I suddenly felt as naive as the day I walked into Kent's bedroom.

"There's no need to be afraid. I won't touch you," he said in a gentlemanly fashion. "All you have to do is get into the car and take your pants off, then your shorts, give them to me, and you get your money. I won't lay a finger on you."

I still didn't believe it, although I knew he meant it. This was one kinky experience Helen had not prepared me for, so I stood there, thinking about it, and he must have thought the price was too low for me to consider because he suddenly went up another ten dollars. "I'm in a hurry, so here's another bill to get you moving."

Thirty dollars for a pair of shorts which had cost me something like a buck? I got into the car, kicked off my shoes, looked around to see if anyone was watching (no one seemed interested), and pulled my pants down and off my ankles. "Ummm, nice," he said, his hands on the steering wheel, his eyes glued to my shorts. I pulled them down and off and handed them to him. "Oh, oh, they're wonderful, so warm," he murmured, holding them to his cheek. Honest to God, that's what he did.

Well, I was spooked. I pulled my pants up so fast you'd have thought lightning had hit me. I got my feet into my shoes and took the thirty bucks from him and started to get out of the car when he said, "They're really rather clean."

"I just put them on this morning," I said.

"Will you meet me Wednesday afternoon?" he asked.

"What for?"

"Another pair of shorts. But you must promise to wear them for the next three days so they'll be nice and soiled for me."

"Yecch," I said, which wasn't the best choice of words to hurl at a customer if I was going into the underwear business at that point, but the thought of having to wear the same underpants for three days made my skin crawl.

"I'll pay you fifty dollars. Meet me right here, Wednesday afternoon, three o'clock. And be wearing them!"

All I could see was fifty dollars floating around in my head. "I'll be here," I said, and started off across the street, toward the post office, feeling self-conscious because my cock was flopping around in my jeans. It was the first time I walked down a street without underwear and I felt naked! (This is funny, remembering how I felt, because today I rarely wear undershorts!) I glanced back to see if he had driven away and I noticed him watching me intently, and I thought, though I wasn't sure, that he was beating off into my shorts while he watched me walk away, turned on by the knowledge that I had come to the corner wearing jockey shorts and now had nothing on under my jeans as I continued down the street.

I went into the Hollywood post office, which is a zoo if there ever was one, and applied for a box so Miss Pearl and Kent could write to me. Then I continued up Wilcox to the boulevard again, and back to the hotel. When I got to the room and woke Paul, who was still sleeping soundly, I had begun to realize I had struck gold. "Wake up!" I cried.

"What the fuck? Why?" he mumbled, finally sitting up.

"We're going into the used-jockey-shorts business!"

You should have seen the expression on his face.

On Tuesday night I took a pair of shorts with me into the bathroom. I took a shit, and then I used the shorts to wipe my ass just a bit, just enough to soil them. I also peed a bit on the front of them, in the pouch, so it looked as though I had been wearing them all my life. I wanted to see if it would work. Paul said I was crazy, but he was anxious to find out what was going to happen.

On Wednesday afternoon I put on the shorts I had soiled (I could stand wearing them for an hour for fifty dollars; I would shower as soon as I got back to the hotel) and walked to the corner of Selma and Wilcox. The guy drove up a minute later and parked the car down the street, closer to the YMCA, where we had first met. I walked up to him and said, "Hi."

"Hello. I'm glad to see you. Won't you get in?"

I got in and I got out of them and he went ape-shit. He was ranting and raving about how dirty they were, how perfect they were, and he got so carried away he handed me another ten bucks on top of the fifty. And we arranged to meet the next week, same time, same place, only I was to sell him my jock strap at that time, so when I left him and started walking back to the hotel without my undershorts, I stopped at a store on the boulevard and invested two bucks of the sixty for a jock strap.

Paul cracked up. He said it was too crazy to believe, and we had better cash in on it before someone else did, but who and how?

The following week, just before I put the jock strap on (I had rubbed it on the sidewalk and boiled it in hot water to make it look used) and took my stroll to Selma, an idea came popping into my head: my post office box! Why not sell used undershorts by mail order? And who else to ask but my expert, the fat buyer?

I hit him with it before I gave him the jock, which was a good idea because he was totally incoherent after it was in his hands. Anyway, he told me he loved the idea of me and my "buddy" selling our dirty underwear through the mail because he had many friends who were into the scene but were not able to get out and purchase off the street like he was. My ass. They didn't have the guts to call a kid over to their car and offer to buy the shorts off his body.

The guy took the number of my post office box the following week and said he would have orders coming

75

in shortly. He also suggested that I place discreet ads in some of the then-underground newspapers, which, if they were still being published today, would make *Screw* look like the *Christian Science Monitor.* So Paul and I wrote up very humorous ads and sent them in (I recall that two of the papers found them too indiscreet to print) and then sent some pretty raw advertisements to local sex rags—small papers which were circulated through sex clubs and in gay bars and the like.

In two weeks we had $267 in cash sitting in front of us, and orders for fifty-five pairs of underwear, and requests for pictures of "what went in them." I swear, had we kept it up we would have become big business, listed on the New York Stock Exchange and all. I had visions of our "factory," where a hundred studs sat around all day beating off into jockey shorts, a whole assembly line, passing them on to the girls who wrapped them in Saran Wrap, then to the mailing room. . . .

We didn't run the ads a second time because the first set wore us out. We finally had mailed out something like a hundred pairs of shorts, all of them full of cum, which meant a hundred extra orgasms which could have netted us at least five bucks each on Selma, but we made a big profit and had a few laughs doing it. Since then, I've suggested it to boys who wanted something to do during the day, and one kid I know in Los Angeles has a monopoly on it. He makes about sixty dollars a week just by sending shorts to people, and that's on top of expenses. A kid going to high school could maintain a nice income if he had the underwear to do it with.

All kidding aside, thank God we had the underwear thing going to keep us laughing, because happy hustlers we were not. Paul was going crazy because we had no money left over after we shelled out for the rent and food; and, because of the way of life we had been used to and the better one we had dreamed about, we were disappointed kids.

I would walk down Selma at night once in a while, just to get the feel of the place, sometimes being hissed at by the regular queens who roamed the area, but more often being offered "rides" and "cigarettes." I kept turning them down, kept fighting that something inside me that every boy fights at some time in his life—his masculinity, his sexuality. I finally gave in, to an extent. I became "trade."

Even today, when homosexuals talk of hustlers they usually are speaking of trade. Those are the *supposedly straight* guys who will let another male go down on them for a price. I say "supposedly straight" because I haven't met one of them in all my years and experiences that didn't, deep down, have a desire to get it on with another guy. I don't know how they can keep telling themselves that they are not homosexual when night after night they are having their cocks sucked by three or four or sometimes more men! They're closet cases, guys who are so afraid of their masculinity that they have to talk about fucking broads all the time, and yet need to make the fags kneel in front of them and suck them off for a price. Usually they end up in a sad and sorry state, on drugs, on skid row before they're twenty-five, in jail, or a bit of all three. I knew a boy who died of an overdose of heroin at twenty-three. He had suddenly started to age, his boyish qualities hardening from all the nights on the streets, all the one-night stands, all the mental anguish he went through to prove to himself that he wasn't a fairy. He was a beautiful boy, bright, he had so much to live for. Many men wanted him to reciprocate in just the slightest way, and they would have set him up well, made him happy. But no, they could touch *him*, but he wouldn't lay a hand on *them*. I said to him once, "Robbie, that guy you've been having on Friday nights, he's a handsome young man! He's practically offered you the world, and you won't take it because you won't touch him."

"He wants me to fuck him in the ass," Robbie muttered.

"So what? What's different about fucking him in the ass or fucking him in the mouth? You say you fuck your girlfriend in the ass. What's so different about doing it to him? A guy's asshole is just the same as a girl's, or haven't you looked?"

77

"Oh, man, Grant, fuck you!" And he got up and stormed out of the restaurant.

I'm guilty of doing what Robbie did, but it didn't put me in my grave. It took me time to come to terms with myself, and often I would think of the gentle advice Helen had given me about bisexuality, and slowly I was able to ease myself into a feel here and there, then touching a guy's cock, maybe even beating him off for another ten bucks, and then finally becoming a truly bisexual hustler, meaning I will do anything with anyone, woman or man.

My first experience took place in the hotel room. Paul had come in one night and told me he had met a rich bitch and she was taking him to Vegas, that she adored him, that she promised to suck him off in the middle of the desert and more. I warned him to be careful, but Paul was big and handsome and strong, and I knew he could take care of himself.

So that same night, after he had packed his bag real fast and joked that he'd write to me, I got up the nerve to walk down to Selma and plant myself on one of the corners. A couple of the guys there didn't like me taking over their ground and told me to get my ass home to mommy, to which I replied, "She's in bed with three black dudes and there isn't room for me," which shut them up. One kid was really very nice. He offered me a stick of gum and asked me where I was from. I told him and he smiled and said he was from Minnesota. "Been here long?" I asked him.

"Few weeks. You?"

"Almost three weeks. Enough to get to know the place."

"Yeah," he said, "I know what you mean." He looked down the street, at a green VW which had just gone by. "That's who I want tonight. I'll be seeing you." And with that he walked toward the car, and, soon after, got in and it sped away.

I stood there for a few minutes, dressed in tight jeans and my sneakers, the Selma Uniform, as it was called, and I guess a new face and cock on the block was needed, because I had many cars slowing down and the drivers staring me up and down, and I was the only one on the street who was getting that kind of reaction. It would only last a night or two, however; a new face appears every day, and the others all fade together after that. I was hot tough stuff for a few nights, and after that I was just another hustler.

It really was easier than I had imagined it would be. A car pulled up and the guy asked me for the time— all the clichés you read are true—and I guessed and told him. He was in his thirties, nicely dressed; he appeared intelligent enough. He made me an offer of twenty dollars and I accepted and I got in the car and we drove to my hotel.

When we got to the room I didn't even bother turning on the light. I let him open my jeans and pull them off, and then I fell back on the bed and closed my eyes while he gave me a wonderful blow job and rimmed me a bit. I came twice because after the first orgasm he started licking my ass and balls again, and I stayed hard as rock. But he didn't give me any extra money.

He got up and left without a word, and I stayed on the bed, naked from the waist down, telling myself it wasn't so bad to let a guy suck me off, a mouth is a mouth. I figured I could do that often, lie back and let guys do me, while I was searching for a hungry widow to come rescue me. I lay there, playing with my cock, and I had to smile because I was once again in the same position I had been each night at Helen's, lying with my hips thrust in the air. Only in place of a woman sucking my dick it had been a man, and so what? I didn't touch him, did I?

I looked around the room and became painfully aware that those four green walls were nothing like the beautifully papered walls I had been used to in Chicago. The window with its torn shade could never match the French windows and beautiful curtains which had overlooked LaSalle Street. Suddenly I wanted to go back, but I hardly had the money to get to Pasadena, much less Chicago. I fell asleep feeling very lonely.

The next few days were hard ones, and they blur together. I had become a typical Hollywood hustler, in the worst sense of the word. I would turn tricks for anywhere from five to twenty dollars, in cars, restrooms, alleys, motel rooms, movie theaters, you name it, I did it there. And one wasn't enough; I had to pride myself on how many I could have in one night. It was almost as if I was so guilty about the guy I had been with that I wanted another in a hurry to relieve that guilt. I needed someone sucking my cock twenty-four hours a day, and when you get into that, you're in trouble. My eyes were red with sex. That's all I seemed to live for, and the only way I could get it was with men who would pay me, and the more I did it with them the more I hated them and myself.

Paul hadn't returned and it had been four days. I had dragged myself into the hotel room around four in the morning and got a call at six. It was Paul. "Tracy, I'm in trouble, big trouble." I had never heard him sound like that. He was terrified of something. "Listen, pal, I just wanted to tell you to hang in there and that I'm sorry . . . I'm sorry I'm not gonna be back right away to help you pay for the room and all."

"*Paul!* Where are you? What's happened?" I don't think I ever felt so sober after only two hours' sleep in my life.

His voice drifted off into sobs and he ended the short conversation with, ". . . I'm going to go back to Helen as soon as I can . . ." Click.

"PAUL!" But yelling into a dead receiver solves nothing. I set it down and leaned against the wall, confused. Then I tried to sleep, telling myself that Paul could take care of himself, but that did no good because I only tossed and turned. I went out into the sunlight and ate a big meal off the money I had pulled in the night before, and then I went to the bathroom and threw it all up. On the way back to the hotel a man stopped me and told me he had seen me on Selma and wanted to know if I wanted the services of a pimp. I told him I did not, that I was sick, and I needed some sleep. He handed me a little pill, telling me it was a little tranquilizer and that

80

it would help me sleep. I tossed it in the ashtray in the lobby of the hotel, went to my room, and slept until dark.

Then I got up, showered, put on my tight jeans, and went out and hit Selma. After letting a guy suck me in his car for five bucks, and another watch me beat off for the same amount, I walked to the corner of Sunset and Vine, and then down to the big Hollywood Ranch Market, where a woman said she saw me steal a bottle of aspirin. The next thing I knew a cop was holding me by the neck, asking me what the hell did I do with the pills I had stolen, dragging me out of the store.

And all I had gone in for was a quart of orange juice, which I really had planned on paying for.

I had a rough time at the police station, the first of many such visits Grant Saxon would make to such places. They couldn't hold me on anything, but they figured my story out nice and fast, and I was "advised" by an old fart in a suit and tie that I belonged back home in Wisconsin, "back on the farm" is the way he phrased it, and not on the streets of Hollywood. "It's a jungle here, kid," he said, which I thought was a better cliché than the ones I'd heard on Selma.

"You're telling me?" I replied.

So, I decided it wasn't my day; I would go home and sleep and try life again tomorrow.

I never made it.

A guy picked me up on Highland Avenue. The reason I went with him was he was better-looking than I was, and he couldn't have been over twenty-five. He asked if I had a place to go, and I told him I didn't. Fact was, I just didn't want to see that damned hotel room again. So we drove to his apartment, just above Cahuenga Boulevard, across from the Hollywood Bowl, and in a few minutes we were naked and he was kneeling down in front of me.

His hands ran up my sides and grasped my shoulders as he sucked my cock, and then he kind of pulled me down to him, and I went. I knew there was going to be a time when I would have to stop fighting and give in, and I figured I might never again be so lucky as to get a guy so good-looking and clean and exciting, so why not?

He held my face in his hands and we were both trembling. "You've never done anything before, have you?" he asked.

I shook my head.

"You've been trade?"

I nodded. "Yes."

"I'll pay you more if you kiss me," he said, and I didn't even think about it. I closed my eyes, opened my mouth, and let it happen. And then, when he pulled back and I looked at him, he gasped and said, "My God, you're really frightened!"

"Yeah, I am," I said.

"Don't be, Grant, don't be," he said, running his fingers through my hair.

I reached down and wrapped my hand around his hard cock and asked him to go slowly as I moved my head down and put his dick in my mouth.

"Oh, oh Grant," he moaned as I started sucking on the first cock since Kent's, a hundred years before.

The guy was gentle and he was kind, and we made love for nearly three hours. I wanted to stay with him the whole night, just to have someone to sleep with, but he explained that he had a roommate and the guy would be coming home soon since he worked a night shift.

So he drove me back to the hotel and handed me some money, which I didn't even bother to count. I hated to leave him because I honestly liked him and because I knew that I would never see him again. "It's been special," he said as I got out of the car.

"Yeah, bye," I said softly.

I shuddered and made a mad dash for my room, and dialed the phone. That's when Frank answered and told me Kent had gone to Europe two days earlier.

And that's when I decided I'd had enough fighting my masculinity on Selma. What I had just gone through with the good-looking guy was no more difficult than fucking a woman who weighed in at 250 pounds and liked to be told stories about me screwing her in a raging storm at sea (one of my steady customers at Helen's used to ask me to do that, honest). It had been, in fact, easier. I had to admit it to myself finally—I liked it. *Look, asshole, you liked it!*

So I had admitted to myself, as Robbie and other trade studs would never do, that I liked getting it on with another guy, and it certainly helped my attitude.

But it didn't help my current situation—the next day I was kicked out of the hotel because I was ten bucks short on the rent. Hell, I hated the dump by that time anyhow.

So I hitched a ride to the ocean, where I found a place for kids to crash, in Venice, and after turning a few tricks and saving some money, I got myself a room, back in Hollywood, and a part-time job in a car wash. I was beginning to get my head back together, although I realized that I would much rather suck a guy's cock than shine bumpers, so the legit job didn't last long. But I didn't have to go the Selma route any longer, now that I would do anything. Once my phone number was passed from one guy to another, all I had to do was stay at home and wait for them to come to me.

Strange things happened in the following months. I let my hair grow and fell in love with a beautiful girl named Shelley. I made enough money to buy a beat-up old Rambler. I found out my mother had suffered a heart attack while doing a revival in Mississippi, and was back at the Reynauld home, resting. Miss Pearl wrote that Helen had never heard from Paul, and I sensed that none of us would ever hear from him again. California seemed to be growing on me, or so I thought as long as Shelley was around, and I seemed to be growing up. A guy measured my cock one night and announced that I had exactly eight inches.

I think it is a very good thing for a hustler or a hooker to have a lover, a girlfriend or a boyfriend. It fills part of their need to be loved, apart from the physical sense, which we certainly get enough of. Shelley was a beautiful, soft-spoken girl who loved me dearly, and for the seven months we were together, I felt wonderful.

We met at a taco stand, which are as plentiful in Los Angeles as cherry trees in Washington. I don't know what it was, just a look, a giggle from her, a smile from me, and suddenly we were walking down the street holding hands. She was very beautiful, slim, small-breasted, with big blue eyes, sandy brown hair exactly like mine, and a smile that could light up the world.

"You a taco nut?" she asked.

"Um, no, not really. I can take 'em or leave 'em."

"What's your name?"

"Grant," I said, not even thinking I should say *Tracy*.

"That's unusual." She finished the last of the Coke she had been carrying in her other hand and tossed the paper cup and straw into a crummy-looking convertible sitting at the curb. "I hate convertibles," she said, "they're dangerous."

"What's your name?" I asked.

"Shelley."

"That's unusual. And I don't think convertibles are so dangerous."

She giggled the same way she had done at the taco place and looked up into my eyes. "I like you, Grant-with-the-unusual-first-name!"

I pressed her hand tightly in mine. "I like you too, Shelley. I really do."

"Let's walk for a while, okay?"

I nodded and we continued on down the street. And another. And another. We didn't know where we were going and we didn't care—we were two kids who had met and fallen for each other, instantly. I can't recall everything we talked about because it was such an emotion-packed night, you know? Full of feelings I had never felt before! And it was the same way with her, she told me she never dreamed that one day she'd be walking around the dark streets with a guy she'd never set eyes on before, and telling him the story of her life. And, more than that, trusting him.

And she did trust me, because she believed me. She believed in me, in my future, and she believed everything I told her, which were mainly lies. I had to lie, didn't I?

I was falling in love and I was smart enough to know, in the foggy bliss I was experiencing, that the truth would kill it. I didn't want anything to jeopardize what we had going for us, and, thinking back, we had so much. . . .

We went to a movie a day later, a cowboy picture, and I sat with my arm around her. It was uncomfortable as hell, but it was something I had never done before, something most kids do every weekend while they're in high school. I bought her popcorn and a Coke and we shared both and every time we reached for the corn at the same time and our hands met, we'd start laughing— in fact, we almost got tossed out of the theater. I never felt such joy being with another person.

After the film we found a tacky little restaurant, a pizza place, and we sat there, not saying much, holding hands across the table with the red bug-killing candle inside its white plastic-net wrapping between us.

"I can see the flame in your eyes," she said.

"What?" I looked passionate for her?

"No, silly," she said, "not *that* way! I can see the flame of the candle in your eyes, it's reflecting. I love your eyes."

I blinked and told her I thought hers weren't bad either.

"They're getting bad," she said with a shrug. "I have to wear glasses at work."

Good opening—I knew she worked nights, but I didn't know what she actually did. "Tell me about your job."

"I work at the *Los Angeles Times*, downtown. I do a lot of lousy little things, like proofreading columns and stuff, typing, doing a little bit of everything. I love journalism, I really do. I guess I want to have my own syndicated column one day."

"Hedda Hopper?"

She grinned. "Louella. Hey, Grant, what do you do? I have a feeling I know."

"You . . . you do?" I started to sweat.

"See, when I said I could see the flame in your eyes, I thought to myself, I hope he's a writer. I mean, you don't have to have actually written anything that's been published, it doesn't matter to me. I just have the feeling that's what you want to be."

I nodded. It was the easiest thing to do. Could I have come up with something better than that?

"Tell me!" she urged, bursting with energy.

"Well, I have published something. You know those cheap westerns, those paperbacks on the stands?" I was looking out of the window of the place, directly across the street at a big all-night newsstand.

"You write them?" She seemed astonished and so damned proud. I couldn't let her down.

"Yes, but they're crap."

"But that's wonderful!"

"Well, someday I'll write something really good. Maybe I'll even write for the movies. A *Casablanca* or something terrific like that." It was my favorite film.

"You like *Casablanca*? I do too!" She put her thumb up to her lips and bit the nail. Her expression changed, she seemed all at once softer and much more serious.

"What is it?" I asked.

"Well, you'll think I'm totally nuts, but I suddenly feel like you're my Youngblood Hawke."

Oh my God. I had read *Youngblood Hawke* at Helen's. In fact, I had read most of it aloud to Miss Pearl while she made dumplings. She had loved it as much as I had. And now Shelley called me *her* Youngblood Hawke, and there was only one possible answer to give her: "And you're my Jeanne."

Her eyes filled with tears and I think that was the moment which bonded us together forever. It meant a lot to her, yeah, but it meant a hell of a lot to me too. I wasn't being facetious when I said that, or merely trying to prove I knew something about literature. I really meant that she could be to me everything Jeanne was to Youngblood, providing love, inspiration, hope, laughter. I hadn't kissed her yet, and I was suddenly filled with the desire to do so. The waiter brought the pizza and set it down, but I didn't even notice. Impulse finally gave way and I kinda stood up and leaned over and kissed her on the lips, gently, and when I sat down again the whole front of my shirt was full of tomato sauce.

86

But I couldn't have cared less.

We dated and we kissed more and more, spending nearly every afternoon together, going to the beach or the mountains, fleeing the city, looking for our very own private world. About a week after we had been going together, we did find that private wonderland we had been searching for, and, oddly enough, it was *inside* us more than in the setting at our feet.

We decided to have an old-fashioned picnic. I dressed in my old jeans and a red and white checkered shirt, which looked very farm-boy, and Shelley wore one of those long granny dresses, a pretty green material covered with yellow daisies. She knocked me out, she looked so fantastic when I saw her come out of her house that morning and run toward the car. She had a big straw hat on her head and her hair was hanging down over her shoulders and she wasn't wearing any shoes. I don't want to sound silly, but she looked as free and lovely as the daisies on her dress. She set the picnic basket in the back seat and got in. "Hi, L'il Abner," she said.

"Hello there, Daisy Mae!"

And we drove off, laughing.

We found a beautiful spot up in the mountains, and if it hadn't been for the lousy beer can I stumbled over when we were spreading the blanket on the grass, I would have sworn the place had yet to be discovered by humans. Oh well, we pretended it was all our own.

She had packed cheese and fresh fruit and sourdough bread and a bottle of red wine. Even two wine glasses, real crystal from her mother's dining room cabinet. We toasted each other, ate ourselves silly, and then relaxed. "I want you to meet my parents," she said as she lay back in my arms. I was sitting up against a big rock in the hot sun, twirling my fingers around through her hair. "I think they'll like you."

"Why's that?" I asked.

" 'Cause I love you so much."

Love me? We had yet to use the word with each other. *Love me?* "Shelley, do you?" I asked softly. I could feel my heart beating halfway out of my chest.

She bit her lower lip and nodded firmly. And she

looked up at me, hoping, I knew, for the same words from my lips. I moved my mouth to hers and kissed her, and then, without opening my eyes, I said it: "I love you too, Shelley."

And then we kissed again, this time hard, passionately, holding on to one another as tightly as we could, rolling around on the blanket in the grass under the beautiful afternoon sun.

"I want to make love to you," I found myself saying as I kissed her chin and her ear and her soft neck. "Oh, Shelley, I want to make love to you. . . ."

"Yes," she whispered, and I could tell she was scared, but that she wanted it as badly as I did. I lifted her dress and fumbled with my jeans—I had never fumbled getting my cock out before, why now?—and ran my hands over the part of her body I had never touched before, and do you know what? It was as though I was feeling a woman for the first time in my life! It was altogether new and different and magical and . . . shit, I can't even explain it.

All I know is I saw stars when I entered her, as if it were the first time I had done that. I knew it was painful for her, and I worried and tried to be gentle, but I could tell at the same time that she loved it and for all the pain, the pleasure was what would be remembered. We climaxed at the same time, in small cries and moans which drifted up into the clouds, and it was the most beautiful moment of my life.

I held her for a long time as she cried softly, and then I asked her if she was happy about it and she said yes, she was. We were both sweating and it seemed to be getting warmer, so we took off our clothes, which seemed a very liberating act for both of us. We were comfortable in our nakedness, which surprised us, and we walked down to the little icy stream which ran from the top of the hill, and put our feet into the water and even splashed some of it onto each other. God, we felt so young and free and open and on top of the world! We danced back to the blanket, where we lay silently for a long time, exploring each other's bodies gently with our fingertips, and then I got hard again and we made love for the second time that day.

It was as wonderful as the first.

Now, I suppose you find this very hard to believe for a kid who's been selling his cock since he was old enough to know what it was for.

You must remember and understand hustling is a business, and that Shelley was something else, something very normal and natural, a lover, a girl I was in love with. So what if I made my living through sex? It was almost as though I went off each night to work at a gas station. What was the difference? She had a job downtown at the *Times*. I told her I wrote my "westerns" while she was at work, and that way we worked the same "shift." I would tell her, "I'm not going to answer the phone tonight, so don't call on your break," if I knew I would be having a trick up to my room. It worked out perfectly and my hustling didn't have the slightest effect on our relationship, except that it often paid for dinner and kept the car filled with gas so we could spend weekends together in Santa Barbara or San Diego.

Behind the hustler named Grant Tracy Saxon there is a person named Grant Tracy Saxon. And Shelley had fallen in love with the latter.

And she is the only girl who has ever called me Grant.

I'm not writing a love story, for if I were I would devote the entire book to Shelley. But I'm writing the story of my life as a hustler, and Shelley figures into seven months of it, but why do I find it so difficult now to put what I felt for her into words? To leave her out altogether would be tragic; to tell you everything about her would be impossible.

Because I really did love her, and when you hurt someone you love, I don't think you ever quite recover. We had as joyous and fun-filled a relationship as any young couple in love. We enjoyed each other's company, whether walking on the beach or sitting in the living room of her parents' home in Westwood, watching *Casablanca* on television. And we did, twice. We were *Casablanca* freaks long before it became fashionable to be so.

Our sexual life was a good one, if somewhat sparse—perhaps that made lovemaking all the more special. The fact was I had to be good in my work, thus I couldn't have sex with Shelley as often as I wanted to, or as often as she would have liked. But when we did share each other's bodies, it was beautiful, because there was something in our hearts as well as in the nerves of our flesh.

I guess I remember the silly, almost foolish incidents best, like Shelley tossing that paper cup full of ice cubes into the convertible. Once we were at the beach, lying in the sun, and a dog came over and peed on Shelley's leg (she had her knees raised and they probably looked like the next best thing to a fire hydrant in the eyes of the poor mutt). She let out a scream and bolted up and by the time I realized what had happened, she was attracting a crowd by standing in front of the dowager who owned "Fido."

"Your lousy dog pissed on my leg!" she shouted. It wasn't often Shelley talked like that. But when she got mad, watch out.

"How dare you use language like that to me?" the frumpy woman with bubble-champagne hair said.

"Your goddamn dog pissed on my leg! You shouldn't bring your lousy mutt to the beach if he's gonna pee on people's legs! Why don't you train him to piss on *your* leg?"

All sorts of people were standing around, laughing, some mothers dragging their little children away from the profanity. I just stood there, on our semiwet blanket, amazed.

"Well, say something!" Shelley muttered, fuming.

The woman gave her a stern look and finally announced, "Young woman, your leg isn't good enough for my pet to relieve himself on."

Shelley—I could see the explosion coming in her eyes —glared at her and yelled, "Someone should shit in your face, you fart-faced old bitch!" And with that she turned around, pulled her bikini bottom down enough to expose her buttocks, and shot the woman a moon!

I died. I mean, Shelley, this soft-spoken, ultrafeminine chick, sticks her bare ass in the old bag's face and makes a whoopie-cushion sound with her mouth. I laughed so hard, and in such utter shock, that I fell to my knees and nearly peed where the dog did! The beach was going nuts, I mean everyone was laughing and talking about it, and even the lifeguard was chuckling. The woman was so shocked by the scene that she was silent, and her dog was running around and around, barking, probably looking for another set of legs as nice as Shelley's.

Things like that. Outrageous things that made me love her all the more.

Once we were in a department store, shopping, and we stopped at a counter where they sold all kinds of nuts—almonds, cashews, peanuts, kinda ritzy nuts, you know, boxed in gold and ready to be mailed to your friends. Tourists buy them, I imagine. Anyhow, there was a dish of delicious-looking almonds sitting on the counter, and, standing guard over them, a frigid-looking cow with glasses hanging from a chain on her neck.

Almonds, by the way, are my favorite nut (next to a few people I've met) and thus I walked up to the counter to take a sample. That's what they were there for. I picked one up with my fingers and popped it into my mouth.

Then the cow went into action, like a Nazi storm trooper suddenly ordered to charge! She took one step to the counter, staring at me as though I had committed a sin, and rammed her glasses to her face. Then she coughed to get our attention and proceeded to give us a lesson in the etiquette of sampling almonds. She picked up a little yellow plastic spoon which was lying next to the dish of nuts (I hadn't even seen the thing) and rapped it a few times on the counter. Then, with a phony smile on her fat face, she scooped out one nice little almond with the spoon, opened her other hand, dropped the almond from the spoon into her sweaty palm, set the spoon down, opened her overweight lips, and popped the almond straight down her throat.

That was how it was done, she was telling us with her piercing stare, and I must say I felt intimidated.

Not so Shelley.

She said, "Oh, that's how you do it!" very sweetly, and proceeded to do exactly what the cow had done, but for one little change; instead of dropping the almond from the spoon to her hand, Shelley flipped the nut off the piece of plastic with her other fingers and it smacked the cunt right in her eye! She couldn't have aimed better, it hit right under her rhinestone-studded glasses and probably blinded her for life.

We didn't stick around long enough to find out.

Things like that, but it wasn't all jokes and games. We would talk of books we had read while walking barefoot in the sand along the coast, or we'd spend the afternoon sitting in my room, making love for perhaps half an hour, and then playing Scrabble, or just listening to music. Sometimes Shelley would add a few words of her own to a column she had typed the night before, and we'd celebrate reading the morning addition at the taco stand where we met in our own sneaky kind of happiness.

But the happiness couldn't last forever.

The problems began when I started breaking dates, or changing habits we had formed after four months of dating. I would suddenly tell her I had to write to meet a deadline for the book I was doing, and I would beg off Saturday night. Of course, Saturday night I was working a job at a party in a rich homosexual's house in the Hollywood Hills. Could I turn down a hundred dollars for three hours when all I had to do was swim naked in a pool and suck a few cocks?

Somehow we even made it through that, through the lies of how I earned a living and why I had to break dates. I reinforced the writing facade by handing her a paperback western I had picked up at the Las Palmas newsstand, telling her I wrote under a pseudonym because one day I wanted to be a famous writer, and I felt that if and when I wrote a really terrific novel, then I would grace the cover with my real name. I would be the F. Scott of my generation, and she was my Zelda.

I never wanted to hurt her. I lied to her because I loved her and because I wanted to protect her from the truth. Never again have I ever lied about what I do for a living; when I feel I'm falling in love or can tell that someone is falling in love with me, I let them know I'm a hustler, and though I usually lose them, I'm at peace with myself. Because I never want to do to anyone what I did to Shelley.

That is why it is so painful to write about her.

Shelley was raised as a devout Catholic, and she had only slept with one other boy before the day we made love on that mountainside, and the first experience had been a bad one. She was fighting Catholic morality within her, and because she lived with her parents, she had to incur their scorn at times when they began to realize we were sleeping together. I didn't know how to tell an almost-virgin Catholic girl that while she worked in the newsroom, I was lying in a sixty-nine position with a guy in a Hollywood motel.

Also, the way our relationship began, the way we just sort of got along and enjoyed each other, there was no opportunity to tell her what I did. I couldn't say, "Now sit down, Shelley, 'cause I have to tell you something you're not going to understand." There was no way to do it! She just took my word for it that I worked nights (which I did, actually) and that I was as straight as the next guy (but in Hollywood, I sometimes wonder if anyone's straight).

There was something beautiful in the way she believed the lie. What I mean by that is she actually inspired me, even though she felt the inspiration was going toward my "writing." Years later I would feel that belief she had in me beginning to surface, and I knew it had been a source of strength through my troubled times. She was always so pleased and proud that I was a prolific young writer (I think I told her I had written four books in as many months) and, more importantly, she was convinced I would be a fine one someday. And since she loved journalism with a passion and had a great desire to become a regular columnist one day, our "professions" blended perfectly. Yes, I was Youngblood and she my Jeanne. I was Scott and she was my Zelda. It was so good while it lasted. Beautiful.

It was doomed, I realize that. I mean, she had to find out someday. I spent hours searching my soul, trying desperately to muster up the courage to tell her there was no hope of our ever marrying, or having children. We never discussed those things, but I knew they were on her mind. And they had every right and reason to be on her mind. Even her parents, in their distrust of me, would call me "son." We seemed to be the perfect young couple, made for each other. Didn't it fit that we should marry someday?

The end came about like this:

I was on my way home from turning a trick, exhausted. He was one of my regulars, an airline pilot, and I had to go all the way out to a hotel near the international airport to see him, though it was worth it because he paid well and treated me like a prince.

I parked the car in front of the house where I rented a room, and just as I started into the place I heard a car door open. I turned and saw a beautiful woman getting out of a sleek red car. "Tracy?" she asked.

Tracy. I hadn't been called that in a long time. All my male tricks called me Grant, and so did Shelley. From what corner of my past was this woman walking out of?

"I know Pearl," she said as I stared at her in amazement.

"Oh, gosh," I said, "I think I remember seeing you at Helen's." She looked faintly familiar.

"Yes, I was there twice while you were with her, but I always had Jerry. My name is Catherine Ann."

I extended my hand, really very glad to see her. It was making contact with the good life of Chicago again, it was reaching back in time. "How's Pearl?" I asked.

"Fine, fine, cooking up a storm. And Helen's never been better. And Lacey, she sends her love."

"Oh, wow, Lacey!" I said, and then I invited her in.

Which was the stupidest move I could have made.

She sat on the edge of the bed while I poured each of us a glass of 7-Up. "Sorry, I don't have any liquor," I said.

"That's all right, I'm not paying for *drinks*, you know." And when she said that it suddenly occurred to me what she was there for! Christ, I hadn't had a woman customer in so long that I had forgotten they existed! Also, I didn't want one—for some damned dumb reason I felt that making it with a woman would be cheating on Shelley.

Now I ask you, was I nuts or what?

I tried explaining that I had just seen a customer and that I was worn out, at least for that night, but she was already tugging at my pants. She had just pulled my cock out when Shelley called, so I let her suck on it while I talked to Shelley, just to keep her quiet. Luckily it got hard, so she didn't complain.

Shelley told me she had just finished work and that she would like to come over because she had a surprise for me. I told her I was deep into a story, but she insisted and finally said, "Oh, never mind, I'm coming whether you like it or not!" *Click*.

Oh, Christ, she was on her way and there was a hot lady on her knees with a good portion of my anatomy down her throat. I tried telling her she had to leave, but she scratched at me and kept my pants down around my ankles and my dick in her mouth. So I figured the only way to get rid of her would be to come, and I tried my damnedest. The trouble was I had come three times with my airline pilot just an hour before. Flying the friendly skies was a very friendly line of work, and it had taken the wind out of me. I remember sweating, cringing, telling her to rub my balls and play with my asshole, anything and everything to try to reach an orgasm in her mouth before Shelley arrived.

Finally I did it! I pumped her mouth full of cum and pulled out of her and said, "Come on, Catherine Ann, you've got to go, you can call me tomorrow, I'll fuck you, I'll eat you, I'll do anything you want, but *please* get the hell outta here!" She seemed perplexed, but I couldn't give a shit how she felt at that moment. She was trying to pull money out of her purse, my semen still on her lips, as I opened the door and pushed her out into the hall. I heard Shelley coming up the front stairs.

"Catherine Ann, take the back way, please," I begged softly, practically shoving her down the steps. "Call me tomorrow," I whispered, throwing her a kiss as she clumped down the stairs, afraid, I think, that she was about to be murdered. A few times I've seen Edith Bunker get frazzled into a dizzy run by Archie. That's always reminded me of Catherine Ann from Chicago, going down those back stairs in her spike heels, wondering why I had thrown her out of my room so suddenly.

"Grant, who was that?"

I turned to find Shelley looking at me, standing next to the door to my room in her sandals and jeans. She was carrying a flat box, all wrapped, with a bow on top of it. She looked lovely—and inquisitive.

"I . . . I don't know," I said nervously. "I heard noise on the stairs and I came out to see who it was." I walked over to her and kissed her on her cheek. "So, hi."

"So, hi!" she said with a smile, and handed me the gift. "What did I do to deserve this?"

"Nothing," she said, walking into my room, "but I figured you're worth it anyhow."

"Wow, a present," I said, looking at the box as I closed the door. I started to unwrap it, unaware of what she was doing at the time. When I got the bow off and started to rip the paper, her voice startled me, the sudden change, the coldness that was now in it:

"Whose billfold is this?"

I looked up and saw that she was holding a red wallet, exactly the kind of wallet the woman had been holding when she pulled out some money for me. Come to think of it, her bag was open as she walked down the stairs. . . .

Shelley was looking through it. "An Illinois driver's license. *Catherine Ann Miller.* A car rental receipt . . . money . . . pictures . . ."

And as I heard her rattle off the contents of the wallet, which I think she was doing in surprise rather than in third-degreeing me on it, I felt it all dying. Any hope I had held for our relationship to continue was quickly disappearing. I had thought it would be because of my male tricks, that one day she would either find out I was a hustler or I would tell her as much. But never in the wildest stretch of my imagination did I think it would be because of another woman.

Shelley pulled one picture out of the wallet and held it in front of her eyes, squinting. She didn't say a word for a long time, and then her eyes filled with tears and she looked at me, confronting me. "Grant, is it you?" she asked, handing me the picture.

When I looked at it I realized how hustlers and hookers can easily fear blackmail. There I was, standing to the right of little dykish Helen, and Jerry on her other side. Both of us boys were naked and Helen had her hands around our waists, her stubby fingers covered with rings, resting very near our hard cocks. Helen had a big smile on her face. So did the boys with her. I didn't even remember the picture ever having been taken.

I couldn't say anything; of course it was me in the picture. I hadn't changed all that much. The face was the same, the body about the same, the cock the same size. Sure it was me. And it was in a red wallet, lying on the floor of my room. I had been talking to someone who had been going down the back stairs mighty fast when Shelley arrived. I had tried to beg off from Shelley's visit until she was forced to announce that she was coming over and there was nothing I could do about it.

Shelley grabbed her purse from the bed, crying softly, and turned around, away from me.

"Can we . . . can we talk?" I whispered.

Suddenly she whirled around and screamed louder than I had heard anyone scream in my entire life. "I HAAAAAAAAATE YOU!" And she grabbed the photograph from my hand and crumpled it in her fist and threw it in my face.

Then she left, running down the hall, and I knew, as with others in my life, I would never see her again. But, unlike any of the others, I had hurt her deeply, and I had not wanted to hurt her, ever.

I placed the red wallet in the hall outside my room, closed my door and locked it. Then I drank some of the 7-Up left in my glass and wondered if Shelley had noticed two glasses sitting on the desk. What did it matter, now?

I took off my clothes, listening to the woman come down the hall and stop outside the door, and, after a long silence, leave again. I sat on the edge of the bed for a long time, talking to myself, telling myself it was better that it had happened, better for both of us. I told myself it was inevitable, it had to happen sooner or later. *Thank God for the wonderful months we've had!* But nothing helped.

It took nearly an hour before I got the courage to open the gift she had given me. Inside was a framed cover of a paperback book. The title of it was *And Along Came the Gunslinger*. I had told Shelley it was the first book I had ever written, and she had had the cover framed. On the matting alongside the cover, she had written: "*And Along Came Grant*—I love you, Shelley."

I set the gift down next to the bed, clicked out the light, and tried to fall asleep.

It was hard to fall asleep that night because I hated myself so much.

And it was almost impossible to pull myself out of bed the following day. The phone rang off the hook, but I covered my head with the pillow. I was numb, wallowing in the shock and sense of incredible loss I was feeling. It was hard to admit it happened, like someone had clicked their fingers and poof! magically Shelley had disappeared from my life. Although I knew it was bound to happen one day, I was nonetheless unprepared for the pain it would bring.

So what did I do, once I had finally dragged myself out of bed as though I were recovering from a seven-day binge? I tried to drown my sorrow in sex. What else did I know? Drink? Drugs? God?

I called a woman I hadn't seen since before I'd met Shelley, a beautiful lady I had liked a lot, or at least I remembered sex with her as being very pleasant. She was surprised to hear from me because I had dumped her without so much as a phone call to tell her I was bowing out for a while. Anyhow, she told me she had missed me and that I could come over as soon as I got my pants on. Hah. I already had them on.

I don't remember the scene very well, probably because I don't want to, but I know I literally attacked her, slamming her down on the bed with all the force in my body, which scared her. But her fright was outdistanced by her lust, and she was helping me to discard my clothes as fast as possible (she had met me at the door in the raw, I recall). Then I positioned myself to enter her and realized I had nothing to enter her with.

My cock was soft.

I had a fit, trying everything to get it up—playing with it, thinking hard about every dirty picture I had ever seen, concentrating on some of the best sex numbers I'd been involved in—but nothing worked. The woman tried sucking it, but got bored soon after. Who wants to chew on a limp dick?

Shelley was in my mind somewhere, but not consciously. It was Catherine Ann who kept appearing, and every time I thought about her I screamed inside and finally I started to rage and nearly beat the poor woman as I still tried frantically to fuck her with a soft cock.

I think she threw me out, but I'm not sure because I was nearly hysterical and can't remember. I know I walked the streets for an hour or so and then saw a guy cruising me and I figured I had been impotent because I had gone to a woman when I should have gone to a man. Yes, that was it, I needed a regular male trick! The guy circled and finally picked me up and we went to a motel. Cost him thirteen bucks to find out he'd picked up a hustler with the world's most flaccid penis.

In the next two or three days I think I tried getting it up with at least ten men and ten women, and I couldn't do it with any of them. So I finally gave up trying, accepted what had happened, tried desperately to understand it, and slowly, ever so slowly, impotency gave way to normalcy.

But it was hell. Living hell.

But didn't I deserve it? I'm sure my hurt never came close to what Shelley was feeling.

Shelley, dear, beautiful . . . oh Jesus, what is the word? Precious. Yes, precious Shelley. Precious and fragile and so easily broken. Would I ever be able to tell her how sorry I was? I doubted it, and having to live with that seemed the hardest part of the entire ordeal.

I still live with it. And it isn't easy. I broke her heart

99

so easily—why then wasn't it equally simple to patch it up? I guess I was learning some facts of life, and I wonder to this day why they often are so cruel.

CHAPTER FOUR

Sausalito To Switzerland—The Good Times

Soon after the breakup with Shelley came my trip to jail for the first time, and I was so used to feeling the punches by that time that I thought, *Oh, yeah, what else is going to happen?* I was numb.

But talking to that other hustler did me a lot of good; it made me realize I had a lot to live for. By his asking me to tell him my life story, I thought as much about my good luck as my bad, and I started realizing things were not as impossible as they seemed. I had been loved for more than my body, and even though it didn't last, at least it had *happened* in my life, I could be grateful for the memories. I thought about the people who still cared for me and about me. I stopped feeling sorry for myself is what I did.

I started giving myself some credit. Maybe I had no right to feel *above* that other guy, to feel I had more going for me than he had, that I had *class* and he didn't, but that's the way I felt and I'm damn glad I did. It gave me a shot of ego, which I badly needed. I became determined to succeed, determined that one day I would be rich and life would be easy, determined to be the best hustler in America. And, more than any of those things, to become a better person and help others whenever I could.

But before I could do any of those things, I needed help—getting out of jail. I had my phony identification on me when I was busted, the card Helen had printed for

101

me back in Chicago. So they got my correct name and wrong age and the big fucking ape who dragged me out of the Rolls and into the L.A.P.D. squad car called me, "Lacey Tracy," which he obviously thought was a very funny pun. I took it as a compliment for reasons he would never understand.

I never did find out what the hell happened to the guy I had been picked up with. Once we hit the doors of the police station, we were parted. Not that I minded, the asshole idiot. I told him it wasn't safe to be doing it in a parked Rolls Royce Silver Cloud on one of the sleaziest streets in Hollywood at three in the morning. But he told me he went there all the time, it was "perfect." Sure as hell was. He handed me the money, dropped his pants, and the minute I got his cock in my mouth the place lit up like the Fourth of July. I found myself staring into a gigantic flashlight and the words of one of the cops, "Okay, fairy princess, time to stop sucking!" were unmistakably clear.

They didn't really rough me up as badly as I'd always thought they would. God, from some of the stories I had heard, they beat the living shit out of hustlers. I often wonder if it was because they knew they could make a good bit of bread off the dude in the Rolls, and thus they would be chancing it if they socked me around in front of him. I guess he paid them off once we were separated at the station house, and went his merry way.

My way wasn't so merry. I remembered the advice of a seasoned Selma queen: "Baby, you don't tell them fuckers nothing, hear? They git you, you don't tell them you know what day it is!" So I played dumb and shrugged when they asked me questions, but I was nothing new or special in Hollywood. So I was tossed in a cell with hustlers, pimps, addicts, and pushers. No one talked to me except the guy who wanted to know the story of my life.

When they came for me I found that the one phone call I had been allowed had done the trick. I put my dime into the phone—the bastards made me use the pay phone and I was sure the fuck glad I had a dime in my pocket—and called the only person I figured could tell me what to do. His name was John Rosebloom and he was a lawyer.

How did I happen to know a lawyer? Many evenings while Shelley was at work, Grant Saxon was watching John Rosebloom's head bobbing between his legs.

His answering service took the call. I swear to Christ, no one in Los Angeles answers his phone. They all have answering services. So I told the chick my name and where I was and yes, I would like Mr. Rosebloom to get in touch with me as soon as possible because I didn't want to spend the next few years at the address I had given her.

When they dragged me out of the cell—what am I saying, dragged? shit, I nearly ran!—I saw John standing in this little room that looked something like a courtroom, or at least what a courtroom had looked like on television. John paid my bail and this white-haired bastard told me I was too young and too intelligent (how the hell did he know I was intelligent?) to be "involved in these matters." Then he blew his nose and we had to wait for him to find a piece of Kleenex. This dumb-looking broad brought it up to him and he thanked her. Then he ordered me to appear at such and such a time, blah, blah, I wasn't even listening. I was thinking about the blow job John would want for getting me out of the mess I was in. I heard the old fart say something about "sex offender" and later, in the hall, I asked John what that was all about.

"You'll have to plead guilty, be fined, and be listed as a sex offender, and maybe spend a few days in the clink."

"Oh God," I said, feeling sorry for myself once again.

"Or," he said with emphasis, "I can arrange to have the whole thing dropped."

"How can you do that?" What a dumb question. Didn't I know by this time that money speaks louder than words and will accomplish anything when you have enough of it?

Driving back to my room, I asked John, "Listen, if you can take care of it, what is it going to mean? I mean what is it going to cost me?"

He smirked. "Oh, a few hundred bucks, but you can work that off if you want. . . ."

103

And I began to learn to pay for things with my cock.

I have never liked cops, although I have serviced a few. And I have never met another hustler or a hooker who had any special affection for the police force. But as the days went on it seemed as though there were more cops in Hollywood than transients.

I decided it was time to split.

It may have been my paranoia, but I thought they were out to get me. As soon as they know you and know what you do, they're out to get you. It can be in the big time, like with my friend Phillip Delaney, whom I worked for in New York. He ran the top stud farm in the country for years, and once the cops knew about it, they chased him all over town. Luckily, he was one step ahead, and was never closed down permanently.

Or it can be in the small time, and that's where I was when I was in California—the small time, on my own, moving from eighteen to nineteen to twenty. Growing up, but still on my own, doing my own hustling, keeping my own books. It wasn't that I couldn't *find* another Helen. I didn't *want* one. For things began to get better after I moved to the beach.

Yup. I piled all my shit in the Rambler one day and drove to Santa Monica, where I found a great little house close to the ocean. It was falling apart, but it was mine and I loved it. I filled it with plants and all different kinds of furniture, gifts from a florist and a few interior decorators and furniture salesmen I knew. What I had to do for those gifts is none of your business.

I became a beach bum and let my hair grow longer than it had ever been. The sun bleached it out till it was nearly blond, and I even tried surfing, but didn't do too well at it. I was always too busy riding the ladies when I should have been riding a wave.

My regular clients referred me to their friends, who referred me to someone else, and soon the phone was ringing off the hook. Nope, I didn't get an answering service. I had to be different. If I wasn't home, let them call back. It was a rather precocious attitude to take, but they usually did call me back.

I didn't need a post office box anymore, now that I had my very own mailbox on the front porch, and Miss Pearl kept it filled with letters. I would ask her to tell me more and more of her life story each time I wrote her, and she did, in a scrawl I could just barely make out, but I swear, I would have gone blind gladly to be able to read those letters. I grew to feel very near to her, closer than I had felt to her when I lived at Helen's and she cooked for me. She sent me a pecan pie for my twentieth birthday, along with twenty little candles, and I invited a few friends over and we sat around and had a good time. The casual, California lifestyle was growing on me.

Kent wrote often, and he called me every once in a while. He was bumming around, wondering if he wanted to go to college or into the Army or what. He didn't know. Mother had recovered from her heart attack and gone back to the South to save souls. Kent said she talked about my father's drinking so much when she was at the house that he sincerely wondered if her "heart attack" had been mere exhaustion and an excuse to get away from her husband for a few months. Many months, as it turned out.

Who cared?

My parents were becoming harder and harder to remember as the days went on. I lived a different life now, and I could thank them for producing a healthy, good-looking, hung kid, for if they had come up with anything less than that I wouldn't have succeeded in what I was doing. But that was all I could give them credit for, and not that it was anything they had planned. How did they know by screwing they were going to produce a kid who would have the attributes required in a good hustler?

Of course, things were not all cheery through that time, 'til I split Los Angeles for good. On one hand, I was able to pick and choose my customers, and most of them were the cream of the crop—actors, actresses, businessmen, a woman who owned a line of cosmetics which I still see in the stores to this day.

But some of the experiences were strange. A guy kept hanging around my house, watching me. I told you there are vice cops who can "feel" runaways, like a dog following a trail with his nose. Well, this guy got a scent from

105

me, but it was the wrong one. I finally got so tired of seeing him casing my place that I walked right out to the street and asked what the fuck he was doing there and why was he harassing me.

He let it out—he was a vice cop (showed me his badge to prove it) but had a special interest in runaway kids, and because I looked so young and because I fit the description of a runaway from Seattle "to a T" . . .

I thanked him for the compliment, that I looked sixteen, and then pulled out my new California driver's license with my name on it and my correct age and my smiling photo. He knew I was telling the truth and I finally invited him in for a cup of coffee and he turned out to be a pretty nice guy. He never had liked vice-squad work, and loved kids, really loved them. That's why he worked on his own time to help find runaways. I thought of him years later when the Houston incident occurred and suddenly the problems of the runaway child interested the nation. I wondered why, so many years before, so few people took any interest in runaways. The cop who had come in to talk with me sure as hell did. So did Helen. Yes, each had different motives and would set kids in different paths, but they wouldn't let the Joey DeFrancos get their hands in there first.

I started realizing that almost every scummy hustler on Selma Avenue is a runaway, and maybe if the problems back home could be solved, fewer kids would end up the way Robbie ended up. I did what I could, I talked with a few young kids I met on the beach, trying to see what their problems were and who I could send them to so they could get help. Most often they just wanted a place to stay and someone to talk to because of the lack of love at home. I let many of them stay at my house during the time I lived there, boys and girls. You would be surprised how that little gesture of caring helped them. In some cases they went back home, really *wanting* to go back home. Other kids knew they could never go back, and I talked them into seeing my friend, the cop, who would counsel them and sometimes send them on to a halfway house or social organization that could help them. I didn't want any medals for what I did; I was

106

only repaying a favor. Helen had saved me. Maybe I saved a kid somewhere along the line.

Often I would get a call from someone I didn't know. I usually told them they had the wrong number or suggested they call a few other guys I knew who were desperate for bread. But once in a while the person's voice really turned me on, and I would say to myself, "I've gotta meet this person!"

Once it turned out to be a woman novelist whose latest book was, at the time, the bestseller across the country. She gave me an autographed copy, which I still have.

Another time it didn't turn out as well. In fact, what it led to was my reason for packing up the car and getting out of town. I guess I was ready to move anyway, ready for a change again, ready for new people and new places. I was getting restless. Although there was snow in the mountains during the winter, I never went up there. I never really went anywhere since Shelley and I had split. I wanted to see Vegas, but never did. Johns and Janes invited me to Palm Springs often, but I never accepted. Then all at once things started to happen and before I knew it, presto, I was gone.

I got a phone call one day asking me if I was available that evening, and the guy sounded nice enough, so I told him I was. We met on the Sunset Strip, had dinner at a very posh restaurant in Beverly Hills, and finally ended up at his huge house in Bel Air, which reminded me of the Reynauld mansion back in Milwaukee.

I couldn't help, as I was dressing, but notice the pictures of movie stars on the walls—all autographed. I asked him what he did, was he a film director?

"I'm an agent."

"Oh, I've never met an agent before."

"You've done more than that." He smiled, sitting on the edge of the bed. I had told him I'd hitch a ride home, but he said the Bel Air cops would pick me up in a minute—I thought maybe that wasn't such a bad idea, perhaps they wanted quick blow jobs in the back seat of the squad car? I have done that before to get out of a jam. As he tied his shoelaces he said, "I suppose you want to get into the business too."

"What business?"

"Movies."

I almost laughed in his face. "You know, there was a time when I was telling myself I was going to be a S-T-A-R, but now that I'm out here, no thank you. Ann-Margret and Marlon Brando can keep it."

"You're terrific-looking. Nobody said you have to act."

I looked at him, almost glaring, you know? "Hey, all I've been doing since I got to this lousy town is acting." I wonder if that bothered him; it certainly wasn't a compliment to his "charms."

"Grant, you're a good kid," he said, and don't ask me what the hell that meant.

What did I need the movies for when I was having a ball hustling? I had my little Rambler, my house by the beach, all the time in the world, and I was getting more money with each trick. Things were going just fine.

Till the "movies" nearly did me in.

I guess a kid in this business takes his chances. Girls are busted on the streets of New York City periodically; boys are hauled off Selma each night and tossed into the can. Punks take photographs of hookers who have steady boyfriends or husbands who don't know what they're doing on the side, and blackmail them; all too often a hustler will find himself confronted with a sleazy character who whips out a Polaroid and the hustler will recognize himself as the person with a cock stuck up his ass and another in his mouth, and then the sleazy blackmailer will ask for money, threatening that copies of the photo will be on their way to the hustler's parents and/or officials if he's underage, which many of them are. I should know. It's a rough game out there on the streets, and you have to keep your defenses up. Most threats of blackmail are just that, threats and nothing more, and if you're strong, you can tell the jerk to get fucked and walk away from it. Although, in a lot of cases, the blackmailer is a drug addict and he needs the money for a fix—and he'll do anything to get it. You must be careful.

But sometimes you just can't tell who's going to turn

out to be a freak or weirdo or blackmailer. I've never been bothered by blackmailers, because either I didn't care whether or not what they were threatening (sending pictures or tape recordings to someone, etc.) would come to pass, or because I was strong and scared them off. But I've encountered some real freaks (and I don't mean the regular freaks, which all madams know about, and to which all houses cater because they are often the best-paying customers) in my time, and the movie producer is one of the freakiest.

The agent I had been with that night called three days later and asked if he could see me again, this time with a friend. I said sure, I would love it; I told him my price, we set a time, I drove up to his house (he was right about the Bel Air police; they watched my beat-up old Rambler climbing those rich hills as if I were carrying a bomb in the trunk), and we had a wonderful time. His friend was a hunk himself, in his late twenties, and I thought I recognized him, but I couldn't place him. I knew he wasn't another hustler, I could tell that, but I *knew* I had seen him before. Then, while I was fucking the big manly guy in the ass while the agent looked on, it came to me—he was the star of one of the afternoon soap operas on television. I had just watched him that afternoon because it had been rainy and I had been bored. It was very funny and I almost started laughing in the middle of what we were doing, because in the afternoon he was a big stud who was trying to make up his mind if he really loved his wife or a young nurse, and at the same time his cousin was dying of some unmentioned disease and he was the only living relative, and the whole time he sat in the waiting room in the hospital, the women were lusting over him. Hmmm. Very interesting. The same night, in the flesh, the same stud was spreading his legs and moaning as I drove my cock into his ass. Today he's a fairly big movie star and he has a lover who is a lousy but famous rock singer who is adored by millions of teenage girls everywhere. You wouldn't believe some of the things I know.

Or would you?

Anyhow, after that night, the agent called again. He

said he and his friend (who was also his client) had a great time the other night, and would I consent to doing something with an older man? Are you kidding? For money I'd fuck him right into his casket. Hell, at least he'd go happy.

So I was given an address in Malibu, right on the ocean, and told to be there in the afternoon, which was odd, but who was I to argue about time? This guy was one of the biggest producers in Hollywood and his name was instantly recognizable. I was rather thrilled to be just driving out to his house, let alone that he was going to pay for my services. Hell, I had seen one of his early films on television the previous afternoon, right after I watched my friend the stud hearing about the death of his cousin and finding out he was sole heir to the entire estate, which seemed to please him in his sorrow. But that movie, oh, man, Susan Hayward, terrific! And I was going to service the guy who produced it! I was ecstatic as I roared up Pacific Coast Highway. If ever I looked happy, it was that afternoon, Rambler sputtering, windows rolled down, my long hair blowing in the ocean breeze, loving living and thinking of nothing but the good times.

Boy, you should have seen me on the drive back . . .

I arrived at the house and parked the car across the street. It was a beautiful beach house which rested partly on the ground and partly on stilts. I walked down the little walkway and rang the bell and I heard a buzzer sound, so I pushed the door open and I heard a voice call to me, "I'll be down in a jiffy, make yourself at home!"

I looked up and saw a large balcony (the house was a basic A-frame) with plants—ivies and ferns—hanging from it. I guessed the man was dressing, so I walked around the big living room and looked at the memorabilia from motion pictures I had seen, read about, or, in some cases, didn't know they had ever been made. But there were costume sketches from a big musical, a signed portrait of the producer in his younger days, and next to it a collage of posters from most of his big films.

I felt almost honored to be in that house. It was quite a trip.

I looked out the sliding glass doors, to the ocean. Though it was sunny there weren't many people near the water, and the waves were still rough from the bad weather we had been having. I walked out on the balcony for a moment and felt the sun on my face and thought to myself, *I wouldn't mind having a house like this someday.*

(I have one like it now, an A-frame overlooking a beautiful slope just outside Aspen. It's a wonderful place to entertain rich ski freaks.)

"You must be Grant!"

I turned to see a little man in his sixties smiling at me. He certainly looked different from the portrait hanging in the living room. His hair was nearly gone, and what was left was snow white. Not that it mattered, but all the recent publicity pictures I had seen of him (he had a very big movie opening soon) had to have been taken ten years before. It never ceased to amaze me how *age* is hated and feared in Hollywood.

And in hustlers, too.

He asked me to join him in the dining area, where wine had been poured and crisp crab salad had seen set in the middle of the table. "My houseboy left just as you were driving up," he said. He was wearing nothing but a bathrobe and was making no effort to keep it closed. I didn't mind, because my agent friend told me I was being paid two hundred dollars for this little meeting, and that was the largest amount anybody had ever paid me. But this guy could afford it, believe me.

We drank and ate (the food was delicious) and all of a sudden he asked me if I wanted to be in his next film. I gave him one of my are-you-nuts? looks. Then he said, "When did you first decide you wanted to be a star?"

"Star?" I muttered.

"Sure, I know why you're here, that's why they all come here. But, kid, you've got more than most, I can tell already. I could tell about Garland; Bacall; Monty, poor boy; Newman, all of 'em, before they were anything. You've got it."

"No, I like doing what I do. I don't have any desire

111

to be in movies." I thought, this is ridiculous, there are boys all over the country wishing and hoping for a chance like this, and here I am saying no, thank you anyway.

"You're just playing the naive-young-stud role," he said, smirking.

I shook my head. "Honest, I'd rather sit in a movie house with a box of popcorn and have a few laughs. I don't want to be in front of a camera."

Then he gave me a sinister stare (probably something he picked up from Cagney or Bogey) and said, softly, "But you'd go in front of *my* camera, wouldn't you?"

I thought that one out. Yes, I was sure he meant he wanted to take some nude shots of me. "Sure," I said, smiling, "anything you want."

He got up from the table and came around and kissed my forehead. "You're going to be rich and famous one day, Grant, but I'm going to have your pictures first, right there in my book with all the others. They'll be asking for your autograph and I'll already have it, written on a big blow-up of your beautiful cock! The fans will pound on your door and I'll have your entire body in the book next to my bed! They'll never know!"

Man, was he fucked up! I really wanted to get out of there, but two hundred bucks is two hundred bucks. If he wanted to talk about my upcoming "stardom," who was I to stop him?

"Come, let's sit in the living room," he said, and we sat down on a soft couch, around a big ship's steering wheel which had been converted into a coffee table. "That's from the original *Mutiny on the Bounty*. Cost me a fortune."

"Wow," I said.

"Would you like to get comfy, Grant?"

"Does that mean take my clothes off?" I asked with one of my sly smiles.

"Oh, of course, we're very informal here, you know!" And he helped me undress. I stood up and pulled off my socks and shoes, my shirt, and then my white jeans. He tugged them down till I could step out of them, but he was staring at my cock the whole time. "My God!" he gasped. I swear, I thought he was having a stroke, the way he carried on. "You're bigger than ————!" (I would name the famous guy he mentioned but I've never seen the guy's dick, so I don't want to pass second-hand judgment. Thank you. This is Rona Barrett in Hollywood.)

He reached up and started fondling me, playing with my cock, and I began to get hard, thank God, and I was secretly hoping he would suck it and get it over with. It was about four in the afternoon by then, and the sun was starting to go down over the water, and the room was filled with a silver glow. I guess I looked pretty good with all the plants and beautiful wood beams behind me, because he said, "This is perfect for pictures!" And he opened a closet door and pulled out a very expensive German camera.

He took a couple of shots of me just standing in the middle of the living room, with the silver sun shining in my eyes, to "warm up," as he put it. Then he made me sit down in the window seat and lift one leg. *Click.* I had to hold both legs apart. *Click.* I had to lie down on the window seat, holding my cock in my hands. *Click. Click.* Then he went out on the porch, his small but hard cock standing straight out between the flaps of his robe, which was a pretty funny sight, and snapped me through the window as I pressed my body up against the sliding glass doors. Then he came inside, knelt on the floor, and snapped shots of my cock, profile, with the sun in the background. He told me those would come out "like silhouettes." He finally had to change film.

I sat there without saying a word, drinking a little more wine, though I don't like to drink all that much, but in California and France that's all people drink, wine, wine, and more wine. I wondered what was going to happen next—was this to be a photo session and nothing more? Fine with me. It occurred to me that perhaps I should have asked for the money up front, but I knew I could never have done that. It would have been embarrassing and, well, tacky.

Damn, I wish I had been tacky that day!

"All right, Grant," he sang, "come into the bathroom now." He led the way.

The bathroom? Hmmm. I prepared myself for a few photos of water sports. Why not? I had to piss anyway.

We went up to the loft-bedroom and I saw, in the place of autographed pictures of movie stars, autographed pictures of studs in the most erotic poses imaginable—I immediately felt very common, although after a fast going-over I thought I probably was the best-looking of the lot.

"In here, Grant, dear," he said, standing in the bathroom.

I took my eyes off the photo hanging above the bed of the naked boy with chains over his shoulders and walked into the bathroom.

"*Grant*, what a wonderful name. Cary should have used that as his first name. *Grant Cary*. Wonderful!" He honestly said that! I figured he was bananas.

My cock was soft once again, and he took a few pictures of it like that, and then one of me dabbing Aramis cologne on it and under my balls. He handed me a towel and posed me much like the famous Betty Grable bathing-suit photograph—half my ass showing and a seductive smile. *Click.* Then he asked if I would "like" to pee.

"Sure."

"Wonderful!" He kissed me on my shoulder and asked me to stand, ready, in front of the toilet, while he adjusted the lens. He got on his knees and said, "I have golden-shower shots of some of the most famous boys in town. You'll have to look at my collection."

(A note here: in the past few years the "golden shower" syndrome seems to have grown. There is a fascination with urine and urination involved with sex that seems hard to explain or pinpoint. I think perhaps we are constantly becoming more jaded, and the old kicks don't excite us enough any longer. We are always searching for something new and different, something just a little more kinky than the last thing we did. So often in the past few years I have heard a boy or a girl, new at this business, say, "He wanted me to *pee* on him!" or, "She wanted to take a leak all over me!" I advise them they'd better get their shit together and learn to live with it, because it is popular and a very definite turn-on for

114

many people, and those customers into that scene will pay good money to be satisfied. Perhaps this fascination with urination was always a part of the sexual drive of man, but till only recently has remained a fantasy. Now it is very real and every house is equipped for it, and any hustler or hooker worth his or her money is eager to satisfy a customer in that line.)

I held my penis in my hand, and though I really had to take a leak, I admit there was something quite stimulating to see a camera focused on me while I was doing it. I started, but my cock was getting hard at the same time, which made it difficult (I have since learned how to pee with my penis in full erection, if the customer wants that). A few drops came, and then a spurt, and finally a full stream. He kept snapping away with the camera, saying things like, "Oh, I love seeing how it comes out of the slit in the head . . . oh, it's so beautiful!"

Then, while I was still peeing, he ran into the other room, setting the camera on the floor next to the toilet, and came back in with the wine glass I had set on the table next to the bed. He dipped the glass under the head of my cock, just as the last bit of urine was flowing, and it was half-filled when I finished. Then, holding the glass in one hand, he took my cock in his other hand, opened his mouth, and put it in, sucking the last drop of urine from the tip. I started getting very hard and wondered what he was going to do with the glass of piss. *He's not going to drink it, is he?* No one had done that in my experience. I had been asked to take a piss on two guys, and once on a woman back at Helen's in Chicago, but no one had ever tasted it. I had been told by Lacey that some customers liked doing that, drinking it, but I was still a bit naive—I really didn't believe it happened. (Today I am not so naive. One of my boys, Tommy, runs a virtual dairy. Each morning he pees into a small bottle, caps it, delivers it in a sealed box to a very rich apartment house where the doorman takes it up to the man who has ordered it. We make a great deal of money off this arrangement, and neither Tommy nor I have ever seen the man who has his "golden breakfast nectar," as he calls it, sent to him each day. We

115

have never contemplated what he does with it, though a little imagination could conjure up some sharp and pretty revolting images.)

The little movie producer stood up and gave me a little kiss on the shoulder again, still holding the glass of warm urine in one hand. And then he lifted it and poured it over my head!

"YOU BASTARD!" I shouted, sputtering, standing there covered from head to toe with my own piss. It was in my hair and on my chest and running down my side, along my leg. I wanted to kill him.

But he fell to his knees and started sucking on my cock and licking the piss on my leg, moaning, rubbing his hands over my wet stomach. I didn't know what to do— I wanted to wash the piss off me, I wanted to come because my cock was still hard, I wanted my money, I wanted to get the hell out of there.

Finally he pulled off my cock and stood up. "Take a shower," he said, and left the room, closing the door.

And I stood there like a dumb schmuck, looking at myself in the mirror, my cock rapidly diminishing in size, my hair all wet with urine, and I said to myself, *How in the hell did you end up in this situation?*

I turned on the water and stepped into the shower, and as soon as I had started soaping my body he came in and helped out, reaching in to fondle my cock and balls. I dumped half a bottle of shampoo on my head and lathered up my long hair real good and rinsed it off. Then, when I stepped out of the shower, he was on his knees with a towel, playing the slave, wiping the wet ass of the king, and I could easily dig that. I tousled my hair while he dried my bottom half, and then he asked if I cared to go back downstairs and I told him I would love it.

But we didn't make it down the steps. On his bed were two big photo albums and I couldn't help but notice a photo of a naked girl and guy in one (it was lying open, for my benefit I think), so I looked a little closer and was astonished to find they were two young and famous movie stars who had just been in all the gossip columns because of their marriage breaking up.

116

What was more astonishing was that the girl was shoving a long rubber cock up the guy's ass. I sat on the bed and started paging through the scrapbooks, and my friend sat on the chair across the room, dressed in nothing but sheer black nylon undershorts, playing with himself as he watched my cock rise again.

Most of the photos were of guys, posing as I had done, legs apart, playing with themselves, many of them pissing —a few stars I recognized right off the bat, some I was sure never made it past the studio gates, and one picture really blew my mind, the star of a very popular nighttime television series on his knees, letting a very young blond boy pee into his open mouth. The series is still in reruns today.

Well, needless to say, I got hard looking at those photos, and I knew my pictures would soon be added to the book, and I felt that I would at least be in good company. I had a great desire to come, now that I was very turned on and refreshed from the shower, and when I looked across the room I saw my little friend holding a big black strap in his hands. "Hurt me a little, Grant, please," he moaned.

I remembered *two hundred dollars, two hundred dollars, two hundred dollars* . . . I got up and took the strap from him, not quite sure I could do what he was asking, because I had never been asked to do that before, only a little light slapping on a fat lady's buttocks. He moved to the floor, turned on his stomach, and pulled his sheer shorts down so his ass was bare. "Hit me, Grant!"

I hit him, but gently. Hell, I didn't want to hurt the guy! I didn't realize that was the point, that was what he wanted. I was pretending to be a seasoned hustler, right? And I couldn't even get into a real S&M scene.

He liked it, but he begged for more, asking be to hit him harder. *Slap!* The strap make a loud, sharp sound on his ass, and I jumped back as he cried out in pain and pleasure, afraid I had hit him too hard.

"AGAIN! AGAIN!" he squealed.

Slap! I hit him, even harder this time, with the strap, then again and again, and I saw his ass getting very red. He turned over and ordered me to jerk off in his face, so

117

I dropped the strap, fell to my knees, straddling him, and beat my dick over his face. He reached up and cupped my balls with his hand and kept telling me to flood his face with cum.

Which is what I did, and it was a violent orgasm, creaming all over his face, and then he took my cock in his mouth and sucked it a little till I finally opened my eyes and drew in a deep breath. When I pulled out of his mouth, I thought it was all over and I had just become two hundred dollars richer. But it was only the beginning. . . .

"Hit, Grant!" he begged.

"Wha . . . what?"

"Sock me in my mouth, just beat me like a drum, make me come!" His eyes seemed to roll back in his head. He meant what he said. Today I know a hooker who does that kind of thing regularly to her best customer, but that day it shocked the hell out of me—in a way it still does, but I don't put anyone down because something turns them on and the same thing turns me off.

However, I wasn't ready to deal with a movie producer asking—ordering—me to beat shit out of him. "LET ME HAVE IT AND I'LL MAKE YOU A STAR! I CAN DO IT FOR YOU! GIVE ME A GOOD BEATING AND SHIT!" He kept screaming and kicking and clawing at me, trying to get my ass over his face.

"No," I said, shaking, "I . . . I can't!" I jumped up and ran down the steps and started getting into my clothes. He was on the balcony, still pleading with me, but I pulled my pants up and started putting on my socks.

Then he came down the stairs, the strap in his hand, and he was boiling. "LITTLE HUSTLER, LITTLE PUNK!" he screamed. I grabbed my shoes and my shirt and stood up, backing away as he came at me. "THINK YOU CAN USE ME AND LEAVE, HUH? THINK YOU CAN COME AND THAT'S IT! YOU PRETTY BOYS ARE ALL ALIKE, LITTLE MOTH-ERFUCKERS!" He came at me with the strap and the tip of it hit my bare arm.

"Please let me go," I said, still moving away, stupidly

backing myself into a corner. "Please give me my money and let me go."

"MONEY? You haven't done anything yet, you haven't done what I'm paying you for. I want a kick, I want your . . ."

I couldn't stand hearing it. "NO, DON'T!" I yelled, and tried to rush past him, since I realized I was in the corner of the room. He was stronger than I had anticipated. He hit me with the strap again, this time catching me right around the neck, which hurt like hell, and I tripped over the shaggy carpet and fell crashing to the floor. Just as I started to get up, he kicked me, hard, and I fell into the nautical coffee table and knocked it on its side.

I had hit my head and suddenly I remembered the basement toilet of that theater on State Street in Chicago where Joey DeFranco had taken a whack at me. I had come full circle. It was happening again, and I could hardly believe it. But this time I was mad, fighting mad, and I held on to the table for a moment, and then turned to face him, ready to kill him.

And then it occurred to me that what was happening was exactly what he wanted. He wanted to get me mad so I would beat him! I could tell because he was now on his knees in the middle of the room, the strap lying on the floor nearby, and he was whispering, almost growling, "Hurt you, did I, big boy? You mad, huh? You good and mad, you cheap hustler? You want your money, pretty boy?"

Instead of hauling off and kicking him in the teeth (which probably would have gotten my two hundred bucks out of him, maybe even a bonus), I smiled the biggest fucking grin I could muster up, raised my hand to my mouth, and blew him a kiss. Then I picked my shoes off the floor while he cried, "NO, NO, YOU CAN'T DO THAT! NOOOOOOO!" and left.

I stopped by the gate and started getting into my shoes, not wanting to cross the asphalt road in my socks, and just as I pulled on one of my sneakers, I heard a crash right behind me and I reeled around.

There he was, standing naked on the walkway, picking

Coke bottles from the carton of empties near the door, throwing them at me, screaming, "FUCKING HUS-TLER! I'LL RUIN YOU IN THIS TOWN!"

I figured the hell with the other shoe, I didn't want to get conked with a Coke bottle. My farewell kiss was better than anything I had ever seen in the movies, and it had really pissed him off—I have never seen a man so mad. By the time I got the Rambler started he was out by the garage, naked as a jaybird, the last of six smashed Coke bottles in his upraised hand, shouting into the late after-noon calm, "MOTHERFUCKER!"

Well, I don't know what the neighbors thought, but I knew I had to get out of there. And I don't only mean Malibu, I mean Hollywood, I mean California.

Hell, I hadn't seen snow for a long time.

I always do things up right. So I ended up in Switzerland, where, you can be sure, there is snow. Here's how it hap-pened:

I called up my agent friend and told him to fuck him-self. I pushed my apartment off on another hustler I knew who had just come into some money from a well-to-do woman. I packed up the few things I wanted to drag with me, and jumped in the Rambler and headed toward San Francisco.

I never made it, in the Rambler I mean. She died just outside Carmel and I grabbed my suitcases and left the rest of the shit in her and abandoned her there to sleep peacefully above the Pacific forever.

I hitched a ride into Redwood City, and then got an-other ride into San Francisco, from a nice-looking guy who asked me for a blow job, which I was only too happy to give since he was attractive and helping me out. Yeah, if I like someone I'll give a freebie. I've always wondered, do dentists fix their friends' teeth for free?

Anyway, he suggested a hotel where a lot of wealthy people stay, the St. Francis, which I couldn't afford. I don't think they would have let me in the place anyway, with my long hair and worn jeans and T-shirt. (My hair has been short for years now, which makes me look younger, but sometimes I miss the days when I played surfer beach bum in California.) So I checked into a little dump off Polk Street, which was a mistake because every fag in town wouldn't let me alone. And I had had enough of guys for a time—I was looking for a woman again, a woman with a fat checkbook. I had that desire to once again become a kept boy. And so what happens? I meet Flo.

Florence Wellington Maxwell, and I'm not kidding. She came from upper-crust British stock, but she fucked like she grew up in the ghetto. Man, she was a wizard in bed, and I often thought, in the many months I was with her, *she's paying me for this? I should be paying her!*

Flo found me about a week after I had hit Frisco. My money was running out and my desire for a woman was superseded by my desire for food, so I took to the streets and found a few men willing to shell out twenty-five bucks each for a chance to go down on me. One Sunday afternoon I was to meet a guy who had had me the night before, in Sausalito, for dinner, and then go to his house there to make another twenty-five. But I never got to him —Flo got to me first.

She came walking down the street as I was hanging around the Sausalito Inn, waiting for my john. I could tell immediately that she was interested and that she had more bread than the guy I was going to see. So I followed her down the street and she stopped to look into a store window, and I stopped next to her. "Tourist?" she asked, with just the slightest hint of England in her voice. She was wonderfully attractive, even though she was near fifty—chestnut hair, green eyes, nice breasts, perfect hips. I knew I could easily get fifty dollars out of her because I was damned attracted to her. When I think of her now, she reminds me of an older Julie Christie with darker hair. She had that kind of chin, that kind of mouth. . . .

Anyhow, I told her I was just bumming around, and she took a glance down to my crotch and looked into my eyes and said, "Would you like to 'bum around' my place for a few hours?"

"Gee, I don't know," I said, my hands in my pockets,

121

playing the big dumb teenager. "I was meeting a guy, and I don't know if I can afford not . . ."

"How much is he paying you?" She was blunt, you had to give her credit for that.

"Thirty bucks," I lied.

"I'll double it," she said, again looking down at my crotch. I think my cock was stirring.

"It's a deal."

And a minute later we were in her Jaguar, winding up the hill to her beautiful Spanish style house, one of her hands on the steering wheel, the other down between my legs.

It was the beginning of a wonderful relationship.

At first I thought that to tell you about my life with Flo would be boring and would read as one long fuck scene, because that's what we always seemed to be doing. But I told you about Shelley, and so I must tell you about Flo. One had a lot to do with the other, although it wasn't till later, years later, that I began to realize that fact.

Correction. Life with Flo was one long fuck scene *and* travelogue. You see, when we weren't fucking, we were traveling (and sometimes doing both at once). I had always had a desire to see the world, probably because I read so much and learned of such exotic places as Tahiti and Tangier, Cannes, the Virgin Islands (I always found that funny—*me* in the *Virgin* Islands). Flo took me just about everywhere the books had, and even a few they hadn't. She showed me the world. Or at least a good portion of it.

In fact, our very first conversation had to do with travel. She was smoking in bed after we'd balled that first time, and it had been terrific for both of us, I could sense it. There was no need to say, "Hey, lady, you're a fantastic lay . . ." We never had to say things like that; we understood each other. So she puffed on her cigarette and started to laugh. She never giggled the way Shelley did, she always laughed, a deep, womanly laugh. She had the looks of Julie Christie, but the voice of Carol Channing, Tallulah, and Mercedes McCambridge all

122

rolled into one. They should only have looked so good! Okay, I'm getting off the track.

Damn, it's hard to tell about a relationship that had so many facets, so many reasons for being!

I asked her why she was laughing and she told me we reminded her of Tennessee Williams' *Sweet Bird of Youth*. I hadn't read it and asked her to tell me about it. She didn't; she laughed again and told me I had just *seen* it. But I was interested, I wanted to know about it. Was a woman from England in the play?

"Why do you ask that?"

I shrugged. "Well, you sound English, but I can't really tell. It's faint."

"I was born in London, the heart of London. But my family, because of some noblesse oblige horseshit involving certain lands we owned and certain chateaus and manors, moved to the South of France when I was only seven. I attended a convent school run by German nuns, and all we spoke was German."

What? "You're in France, you're English, and you talk German?"

"Hell, you think that's bad?" she asked with another laugh. "The cook was from Italy and if we wanted to snitch any food from the old bitch we had to learn Italian."

"Jesus," I said. It suddenly dawned on me that Europe must be a lot like the United States, I mean size-wise. People cross from country to country just the way we drive from state to state. I could barely imagine speaking one language in Iowa and another in Missouri. And God only knows what kind of mumbo-jumbo they'd speak in California.

"I learned a little Russian too," she said, and my eyes lit up because I had always had a secret desire to see Russia. I had found a book on Russian history at Helen's in Chicago and read about the czars with a kind of open-mouthed fascination. I remember thinking to myself, Christ, I've been brought up my whole life thinking Russia means Communists and terrible people, people without a history prior to the time of Lenin or one of those gents. "Have you ever been there?" I asked.

123

She nodded yes, as though I had just asked if she'd ever visited Pasadena.

"You've been to Russia!" I gulped as she nodded again. I could tell she was becoming very taken with my child-like fascination for other places. I moved close to her on the bed and took her free hand and held it and said, "Tell me about it. What's it really like? The Hermitage. The Kremlin. St. Petersburg . . ."

And she talked about Russia for nearly an hour. At the end of the conversation I found that my legs had fallen asleep. I'd been sitting cross-legged on the bed, entranced with her tales of the people, the snows, the cities, and the smells of the Soviet Union. (I still haven't been there, and it remains on the top of the list of the countries I'd most like to visit. An impossible dream, maybe, but I think perhaps next year I'll hop an American Express tour. . . .) I tried to get up but I couldn't, so I just kinda fell on top of her, which wasn't a bad place to fall, and we started making love all over again.

The second time it was different. I had a complete fantasy. Flo was a Russian empress and I was a low sort of chap, a common worker from her summer home near the sea. She spent only two months each year there, and I lived and worked only to feast my eyes upon her for those eight weeks. Then, one afternoon in the sunlight, on the grass near a large tree, she fell into my arms and asked me to make love to her.

I don't know what the hell Flo was thinking, probably *this stud's not bad for a second shot within an hour*, or something like that, but for me it was glorious. I could picture her many skirts and petticoats being lifted and how difficult it was to get my cock out of the buttoned fly of my coarse work pants. It was some turn-on, and I know it was one of the best lays I've ever had. When I finally came, the scene faded from my mind and I was back to reality, and that reality wasn't so bad. I had the feeling that I had stopped running. And indeed I had. But it was ironic that I'd stopped running by meeting someone with whom I would do almost nothing but travel.

I wonder if Flo had a premonition of her death? I've

124

thought about that a great deal—it gives me an answer to the question: Why did she run around the globe as though tomorrow would never arrive? She lived like Auntie Mame, and I was her Patrick. And in some ways I loved her.

Some ways. How the hell do I explain that? Sure, the physical side of the relationship was perfect, she had a great body for a dame of fifty, fine tits, tight ass, delicious cunt, and she knew how to use them better than most professional girls in their twenties. It's the other part that is hard to explain. The emotional attachment to Flo. The constant need to be with her night and day. The security I found in being with her, and the fear I had of her leaving me.

Is there such a thing as love on the rebound? Does a guy, after he's been in love with a girl his own age, really in love with her, in love for the first time in his life, fall for that same type of girl the next time? Or would he go for the total opposite, someone older, wiser, different? Flo was the antithesis of Shelley. How can I put it without sounding like a real fruitcake? It was the difference between a naive, pure love, and a worldly, wild one. Shelley and Flo. A freshly picked, fragile flower as opposed to a deep rooted, weathered but beautiful willow tree. Flo needed no support, she stood her ground and had for a long time. Shelley needed care, concern, a tenderness Flo had no need nor use for. Which love was more important to me, which meant the most? Well, I've always loved flowers and find them special; I take strong towering trees for granted.

There was some mothering in my love affair with Flo, I know it. That's always been a part of my life—Mrs. Reynauld, Helen, Pearl—and probably always will be. Flo was a strong woman and she loved mothering me all I wanted. She would take me shopping in Venice and buy me a complete set of clothes, from underwear to a fancy-brimmed Italian hat, and then we'd go back to the hotel and make love. Like crazy. I would be her son, her little boy, for an hour or so, and then I'd be her old man, her stud, in bed with her. It was odd, but the link

125

between us was a strong one and we lusted after each other in body and spirit, which is quite a combo.

I put Shelley out of my mind completely. It was easy to do now that I was no longer impotent, that I was no longer running away from anything, that Flo was constantly keeping my mind on other matters—plane tickets, reservations, concerts, operas, parties, balls—and fulfilling every wish I could have for a good sexual relationship. I felt no need nor desire to trick on the side. Fucking Flo Maxwell was satisfying enough, and because she was so goddamned full of energy, I don't think I could have found the strength to get it up for someone else after a workout with her.

And she talked. And I listened. I thought *my* life had been interesting? Shit, think again, Grant. She told me tales of that convent that would make Mephistopheles' pointed ears burn. She related the "shocking" divorce of her parents and the scandal her mother caused by living out of wedlock with a man, and then, after the divorce, with a female lover. About her unhappy marriage to a fat man who gave her money and trips to Paris, but little love. About her work as a nurse in Africa (she plunged into that after her husband died, in an effort not to go crazy from idleness and the knowledge that in her whole lifetime she hadn't done one lousy thing of any worth). Then she came back to America when the elephants and diseases of the Congo became too much for her to bear, and raised money to found an orphanage in Baltimore, where she had lived for many years. Once that project was completed, she felt she had done something worthwhile for a change, and she decided she was going to be reckless and have fun from then on. Why not spend the millions the fat man had left her? And as long as she liked young studs, why not buy some of them too? Whatever makes you smile.

I made her smile—more so, she said, than any boy she had ever been with, and she had been with quite a few. I believed her then and I'd like to still believe it now. I knew she was in love with me. And it wasn't the money she spent on me and the foreign cities she showed me that told me she loved me. It was the look in her eyes just before she'd have an orgasm, when she'd look straight up at me, into me, through me, and then close her eyelids tight and let out the same wonder-filled cry that always told me she had reached a real orgasm. I've had too many women fake it, and I've been guilty of faking it too in some cases, although with a guy it's a hell of a lot harder—I mean, there's tangible evidence! But if you work it right and say something like, "I don't wanna pull out, let it get soft inside you," or something like that, and slosh around a bit, chances are she won't know if you came or not. Or at least the dear ladies I've done that to have been kind enough not to inform me I'm a lousy actor.

I remember one night we were home in Sausalito (which was actually one of seven houses she owned, but to me it was home because that's where we first made it together) and she asked me to let her watch. I fucked her for a few minutes, but she really wanted me to pull out and beat off for her. She put her head up real close and watched as the jism spurted out of the tip of my cock and ran down over my fingers and my nuts. She felt the cream with her fingertips, staring in quiet wonder at the sight. Then she looked up at me, at my sweaty chest and tightened muscles, and said, "Don't ever leave me."

Now, by any stretch of the imagination, that's not the kind of thing a person says after culminating a passionate sexual encounter, be it fucking, jerking off, sucking, or watching. But that's the kind of thing it was with Flo and me; the sex was part of something bigger, something more substantial. It was as though she never wanted to see another orgasm but mine, as if my cock was the only man's organ she ever again wanted to feel inside her. She whispered that to me many times, and I did believe her . . . and found myself loving her, in that completely different way that I described, not as a replacement for my younger, purer love for Shelley, but as the next step. I had lost the love of my life—so why not settle for the next best thing?

And you know what? This is crazy, but it shows you how far I had gone, how taken I was with her: I was seriously considering—just as I had done about a week before the break-up with Shelley—giving up hustling and settling down and maybe even marrying. I no longer felt as though I were a kept boy. I deluded myself into believing I was Flo's lover and we would never part. We would live together forever. Who cared about the difference in our ages? We didn't, and that's all that counted.

I never dreamed it would come to a crashing end one day—one day too early.

There is a lesson to be learned in the story of my life with Flo: No hustler, if that's really what he is, should become too attached to one person. There is always the risk that the one person will be here today and gone tomorrow. No matter how much you feel the woman (or man) keeping you loves you, another boy can come along, another boy just a bit cuter than you are, or stronger or prettier or bigger or God knows what, and *shazam!* he's taken your place and you're back on the street. That's happened to me a few times, and more often to guys I know who just won't learn from experience.

In the case of Tracy and Flo, it was even more disastrous—she died. There she was, at my side, standing on skiis in Switzerland, and the next moment I looked, she was gone. I try to joke about it now when I tell it, because that's easier than recalling the pain of seeing her linger between life and death for three hours before she was finally given peace. I said she was like Auntie Mame, so I tell people she "fell off a fucking Alp."

Isn't it easy to cover hurt with laughter?

Flo had slipped, even though she was an expert on skiis, starting down the slope in the wrong direction, at the wrong angle. After they had pulled her body from the tree she had hit with terrible force—a branch had gone all the way through her—they took her to the infirmary and a doctor was called, and the poor man did all he could do, but I kept thinking, I know her and she doesn't want to go on, I know she doesn't want to fight. I prayed for her to die. I finally walked out of the room when the priest anointed her with some blessed oils and I could still see the trail of blood in the snow leading to the door where we had brought her. I put my sunglasses on and the bright red turned purple and I felt relieved because it was no longer blood but grape juice or Kool-Aid or something like that. . . .

And then it hit me, smack, as though I had hit the same tree. I had prayed for her to die. But with her death I was left alone and nearly penniless in the middle of Europe. No, another boy had not come along. Flo hadn't dumped me for another hustler. But there I was, in the same position I'd have been in had that happened. For all my goddamned intelligence and experience, I had been pretty fucking dumb to allow myself to be without any security whatsoever. I had a ski jacket, a little suitcase full of clothes, a head full of worries about what the hell was going to happen to my life (again!), and a lot of sadness in my heart.

I missed her, but it was easier to bear than the loss of Shelley had been. For one thing, she was gone, she would never breathe again, and Shelley was somewhere in Los Angeles, she was still able to feel hurt and horrified and hateful. Flo was at rest, and she had lived a full life. I had lived some of it with her, and I was glad of that— but I never so fully realized what beng "kept" meant until that day when I kicked the snow around and muttered to myself that I would never look at a damn pair of skiis again. (A promise I broke but good when I bought the house near Aspen—I ski all the time now! I think Flo would have liked me to do that.)

I had put all my security into the woman who had been keeping me. She had been paying me cash at first, in the days of tales of trips to Russia and a wonderfully rich and crazy bohemian life in Sausalito, but once I moved in with her for good, she paid for my sexual acrobatics with fine food, clothing, travel, anything I desired. That sounds far out, right? Yeah, sure. See what happens when your old lady or sugar daddy isn't adding to a bank account (which is in *your* name, by the way) every week. I had a fur coat and fifty dollars in traveler's checks in my pocket when Flo died, and that was the extent of my assets. I couldn't even get back to the house in Sausalito to claim my things, things that really belonged to me! How the hell could I prove I had anything there? Flo had a brother in England, a stuffy fart named Sir Fenwick Maxwell, who should have been the one going down the slope that day. He told his Alfred Hitchcock-like butler to inform me he could not "recognize" me as having been an "associate" of his late and much-loved sister. Much-loved my ass. She hated his guts because he was a man who hated people more than W.C. Fields hated children, and detested her because she never became the nun their parents had planned on having in the family. But *of course* he was bereaved upon hearing of her death, and immediately got his attorneys over to the States, to all seven houses, to all the bank accounts and land holdings and even the goddamned cars—his grubby fingers were touching everything. There was no legal way I could collect even a toothbrush.

But in the end, Sir Fenwick got his end of the stick too, right where he deserved it. Flo hadn't put me in her damn will, but she hadn't put that motherfucker in it either, much to his British dismay. She left it all to charity (which made me smile bitterly because I considered myself "charity" at the time the will was read), and that meant I was stuck.

'Course, I found all that out later; my immediate problem was getting out of Europe. And you don't hitchhike across the Atlantic.

Back to five-buck blow jobs, Grant . . .

I have often had long talks with my boys, or boys who have come to me for advice, and I warn them about being kept. Unless you can begin building a bank account of your own and have your own apartment—year's rent paid in advance, please—and other provisions which you can be assured will remain yours when the sugar daddy keeping you either runs off or drops dead, don't get into it. Unfortunately, most boys do not take my advice, and I see them weeks, months, even years later, but they are all in the same situation—cut off, lonely, without a cent in their jeans, hungry. Experience is the best teacher, but it is often so damned cruel. Hustlers are humans and our emotions are the same as the emotions of anyone else—we love and care and are sometimes hurt, we cry and we laugh, we want friends, we have enemies, we are people. We all too often trust people more than they deserve. I used to give credit quite freely, until I tried to collect some of the back pay due me. I've seen beautiful young boys let their hearts open up to a certain sugar daddy or rich widow, only to have them crushed when daddy or widow throws them out to the street. There is such a vulnerability in man, and any good hustler must somehow try to keep on his guard and realize that reality is often very different from what it seems. It sometimes comes as a shattering blow to realize that, after all the months you spent with the person who was keeping you, he or she only kept you because of your pretty face or your big cock or your tight ass. All that time you had been thinking you were being kept because of *you*, because the person *loved* you, and that outward sex was only a manifestation of the *inner* feelings. Oh, man, an experience like that can be so painful, and, even worse, it can harden a person who is very vulnerable to such a point that he becomes unable to love or trust anyone for the rest of his life.

Maybe the reason I've been able to stay happy in this work for so long is that I understood all that all along, and thus was always able to pick up the pieces and continue.

Another bit of advice I give my boys is: If you give your heart to someone, give it to a person who isn't paying you. Fall in love with anyone but a customer! Don't believe for one moment that the money, the clothes, the plane tickets, don't ever believe any of that stuff is being done out of love (even if it is). That way you'll survive. And if you have a lover on the side, all the more happy you'll be!

Admittedly, I wasn't too happy when I was stuck in snowy Switzerland, realizing I was starting from scratch once again. That can get a guy down, you know? But in the few days after her death, as I took long walks alone and sat morosely by the fire in the lodge at night, ignoring anyone and everyone, I came to realize that there was no sign of the pain like the kind that had come with the end of my relationship with Shelley—the pain that I felt

131

every time I thought about her. I wondered if I hadn't opened only my legs to Flo, and not my heart. No, that wasn't it, I loved her in a very different way from the way I had ever loved anyone, but I was able to take her death well. Yes, I was all bent outta shape about being broke and all that shit, but as for knowing I wouldn't have her with me any longer, knowing the travels had come to an end and the deep-throated laughter I'd become so accustomed to hearing in bed would be gone . . . I somehow found that very easy to accept. It had been wonderful, I had been lucky to experience it, and now it was over. I think that attitude came directly from Flo herself. That's the way she would have wanted me to think. "Live like a sonofabitch," she'd say, "no matter what happens, no matter who you're with."

Well, sure I'd keep on living. I started walking with a smile on my face, and at night, by the fire, I'd look up and talk with other guests and most of them would be very kind because they knew Flo and I had been there together for nearly a week and naturally they were gentle. They helped. People always come to the rescue. I believe in them better than I believe in dogs and cats and plants and favorite phonograph records or a special cake. There's nothing like a person to see you through a bad time, hold your hand, give you some help, maybe just let you know they're there at the other end of the phone. I like people a lot.

And so did Flo. God, she was a wonderful woman. Hey, I think that's the word. She was really a *woman*. She was vulnerable and yet she was strong. She was totally feminine and then there was that gravel-Gertie voice. The pussycat and the tiger. She had vitality and vigor and class, and she fucked like she lived—as if tomorrow would never come and we had better get it all in today. I've asked other guys who they think the most womanly woman is in the world, and the answers vary from Liz Taylor to Princess Grace to Angela Lansbury. My answer is Florence Wellington Maxwell. Her warm thighs and luscious breasts are forever locked in my memory with her supercharged lust for living. What a woman!

And what a mess I was in.

But didn't I say the guests at the lodge were good to me? There was a man staying there, a German physician (and his wife), and he asked me to dinner alone one evening, on the pretense of cheering me up and the fact that he was forced to dine alone because his wife had a cold. I thought, well, you're a doctor, give her a pill. He pried a bit into my relationship (as he called it) with Miss Maxwell (she never used "Mrs." after fatso died) and I explained (just as annoyingly coy) that I had been "accompanying" her. It was a pity, the accident, and I agreed with him. And then he asked if I thought his wife was attractive. . . .

She recovered from her cold awfully fast. I was in bed with them by midnight. No, that's not quite true. They invited me to their room, or I should say he did, and I found it had its own fireplace (hey, I'd always thought Flo got us the best!), which we sat in front of, on the floor, swapping stories about our lives. They spoke a wild cracked-American English, and I didn't understand a word of German, so we giggled through the rough spots. Johannes, the physician (he was probably a veterinarian for all I knew), came from a family of preachers, and he wanted to know all about my parents, but I myself didn't know much about my parents. Hedwig, his wife, told me what it was like to grow up on a farm in Bavaria, and her description of mornings in the mountains in spring made me think of the beautiful opening shot of the mountains in *The Sound of Music*.

But, before long, enchanted as I was with hearing about cowbells on hillsides and wild flowers growing along the rivers running from the melting snows, the conversation turned to sex, and all Johannes wanted to know before he paid me to screw his wife in front of him was, "Are you Jewish?"

"No. But I'm circumcised."

He didn't seem to mind that at all, just so I wasn't a Jew. So, at about one o'clock, he settled back against the bed and watched while Hedwig and I went at it for about two hours.

And I walked out of there about twenty-five dollars richer.

And that's the way I made it across Europe, and finally back home again. I tricked my way from Zurich to Munich, up to Oslo, to London, and finally into New York. No sooner had I stepped off the plane at Kennedy than I was letting a twenty-seven-year-old guy dressed in a business suit suck me off in the back seat of his station wagon in the parking lot near the Pan Am terminal.

He gave a good blow job and told me he was from Queens. I don't know if that happy experience did it, but I decided to spend some time in New York. Why not? Did I have any other place to go?

CHAPTER FIVE

Me, A "Madam"?

I remembered, taking the cab into Manhattan, the tales Paul and I had heard of the money to be made on two streets in the good old U.S.A. *Hollywood Boulevard and Forty-second Street.* I had seen the first and it had nearly killed me. No way was I going to end up a cheap Forty-second Street hustler. I made a vow to myself that if things got rough in New York I would jump a plane back to Chicago. I guess I knew I would end up back in Chicago someday, the place I had really begun my work, the place where I had felt as comfortable and secure. But I had to live through New York first, and I'm glad I did because I don't think I'd be where I am today without my New York experience.

If you can make it as a madam in New York City, you can make it as a madam anywhere in the world.

One thing I noticed about New York right off—it was still uptight sexually. None of that freedom, no drop-your-pants-at-a-smile attitude that exists in California. Oh, the sexual revolution was on, but none of those guys who had wives and kids on Long Island were gutsy enough to wave down a boy or girl on the street. There is something clean and discreet about using the services of a good house, and men will always want that (so will some women). Prostitution will never die, no matter how sexually free we become—proof of the statement lies in Scandinavia. Is there a more sexually open atmosphere anywhere on earth? Most likely not.

135

And yet whorehouses thrive. The "oldest profession in the world" will be going strong when we are long gone, and only the end of the world will close the doors of the houses and deaden the phones of the stud services.

I sat on my suitcase in the East Side Airlines Terminal building and did some heavy thinking. I had learned not to plunge blindly into a new city; now it was time to think about where I was, what the situation there was like, and how I would approach it. I had some money left from the tricks I had turned in London (oh, man, the British are cold lovers, I sure found that out in London —I often wondered where Flo's hot passion for sex came from) and I wanted to spend it wisely, or maybe I should say "invest" it wisely. I wanted a future in New York, not a funeral.

In my travels in Europe I had met some of the best madams going, and visited some of the best brothels. We talked "shop" in many cases, and often I would hear mention of two houses in New York City which seemed to have a fine international reputation. However, I did not know if these houses were strictly girls only, and I considered it a pretty tacky thing to walk up to the door, ring the bell, and ask for a job. I needed a reference if I wanted to make the big time in New York. I had the list of about fifteen rich men and women (and in some cases husband-and-wife teams) from New York who had said, "If you're ever in the city, give us a call!" I knew they were potential steady customers, and I considered asking them to lead me to the best madam in the city, but that too had little class to it.

So I called Helen in Chicago.

She sounded thrilled to hear from me, which pleased me. I had not talked to her since I'd left her, although I had kept in touch through Miss Pearl. Helen had to interrupt our conversation many times to switch to another call—something I would come to know well. The guy running a stud service is just like the madam of a big house—plagued by ringing phones. But I don't put them down, for phones mean customers, and customers mean $$$.

136

"Helen, I want to get set up here, but I want a place like yours."

"Tracy, there's no place like mine." She giggled. I could just picture her sitting there in her muu-muu, her stubby legs crossed at the ankles, her hair piled high atop her head, her fingers almost hidden behind the many rings. I adored her.

"Well, is there something that comes close?"

"Sure, honey, but tell me something . . ."

"What?"

"Are you into everything now? No more women-only crap? Into *everything*?"

I wasn't quite sure what the emphasis on *everything* meant, but I said, "Sure, of course. I grew up."

"Good. then I know the place for you. His name is Phillip Delaney and I think he moved into that famous building. what the hell is the name of the place? United Nations Plaza or something, you know. where Johnny Carson lives. Truman Capote too I think, the place where Bobby Kennedy lived."

"Yeah, I know, I've read about it."

"Well, it doesn't matter, 'cause all you need is the phone number." She gave it to me and told me she would call ahead and tell Phillip I would be calling. I wondered why she wasn't sure of his address--wouldn't a guy running a big house full of studs have a permanent location known to everyone in the trade? I mean, as soon as you mentioned Helen's place in Chicago, the words LaSalle Street bounced into your mind. "Baby, the heat's been on hard lately." Helen explained, "and Phillip got busted about a month back. But he always opens up again, usually in a better spot."

I talked to Miss Pearl for a few minutes and she promised she would send me a pecan pie as soon as I sent her an address, and then Lacey got on the line and said, "How are ya, my crazy little hustler, huh?"

Her crazy little hustler was just fine! I was twenty-two years old, it was a warm August, 1969 hadn't really been such a bad year so far, even considering Flo's unfortunate demise, and I had everything to look forward to. New York was at my feet, and I was determined to conquer it.

I checked into a hotel just off Times Square for one night. I wanted to do two things: give Helen time to call Phillip Delaney, and make myself presentable. No matter how a person is dressed, flying across the Atlantic will make you feel as though you've slept in the same clothing for seven weeks rather than seven hours. I showered and shaved and had the new outfit I'd bought in London pressed for my appearance on Phillip Delaney's doorstep the next day. I put on my jeans and walked to a theater-ticket agency and got a ticket to see Pearl Bailey in *Hello, Dolly!*, my first Broadway show. I grabbed a hot pastrami on rye and went back to the hotel and called Phillip. He seemed pleased that I had called, telling me Helen never let him down before, and could I come over in the morning for coffee and rolls? And Helen had been right, One United Nations Plaza was the address.

I was bristling with excitement that night, seeing the play, walking through the throngs in Times Square, strolling down Forty-second Street with somewhat of a snide expression on my face as I saw the hustlers lined up as I myself once had on Hollywood Boulevard and Selma Avenue. I felt sorry for some of them, the ones who looked as if they were bright, well-meaning young guys, the ones who showed some promise. But I knew if they were not strong-willed with a desire to succeed and be happy, they would soon age, physically and mentally, and soon they would start with needles in the arm. . . .

As with any profession, a hustler must be reaching toward something, not running away. To hustle because you want to forget about your terrible family life or a broken love affair is dangerous. To hustle because you enjoy pleasing others and you sincerely like making use of your body and your sexual technique to make money, that is a good reason. Some prostitutes are suburban housewives by day. If they turn tricks because they hate their husbands, hate the responsibility of children, hate the boredom of a station wagon and a house that looks like all the others on the block, they're going to be in trouble one day, and they're not likely to be very good hookers. But, on the other hand, if a young wife and mother loves making love, enjoys having sex, and knows she can supplement her husband's income at the same time, she has a good chance of doing well in the business, and her customers will sense the pleasure she gets from her work and will tip her well and keep coming back for more. It makes no difference whether or not she works on her own or with a madam, in a house of prostitution or in her garage, her attitude is what will make her a good hooker or a bad one.

It is the same with studs. In the three years I have run the biggest stud service in the country, I have been able to weed out the boys who sincerely didn't like what they were doing, and I have kept the ones who love it. That's the secret of running a good house, and I don't think any hustler or hooker can be so fine an actor or actress that they can pull the wool over the customer's eyes for very long. There will come a time when a customer will comment to the madam, "Sarah's getting tired of me, I'm afraid. I don't know what it is, but I get this feeling. . . ."

And the madam has to let Sarah go.

With boys it is a bit easier for a customer to tell he has a stud who isn't very happy at what he is doing—his erection will be that barometer I spoke of. Once it starts to weaken, the customer wonders. Once it falls, the customer gets mad. And you have to let the boy go.

So I felt sorry for some of the guys I saw on Forty-second Street that night, because many of them would end up as Robbie ended up—I don't really know what happened in Robbie's case, the details, but to know he overdosed on heroin is enough—and others would go the other route and become screaming queens, moving from bar to bar in search of tricks, a dollar here, a dollar there, their existence becoming nothing more than a third sex, not quite men, not women, certainly, and not even homosexual, really . . . just a third sex, prowling the

139

underworld of the big cities until they fade away and others take their place.

When I got back to my hotel room it wasn't even midnight, but I wanted to get a good night's sleep and be ready to greet my prospective employer in the morning. I had a raging hard-on when I fell into bed, but I resisted the temptation and did not beat off—I wanted to be *good* the next morning.

And I was.

Phillip Delaney, to my surprise, turned out to be thirty years old, tall, dark, and handsome, if I can use that terrible cliché. There was no other way to describe him. I knew immediately how he had started in the business— a "Helen" somewhere had taken one look at him and realized she had a money-maker there. And he had worked his way up. In the two years I worked for him, I watched his every move, listened to all his advice, and grew to respect him with the same mild adoration I have for Helen. It was Phillip Delaney who let me work my way up to a position as top stud in his organization, and when he began to go off on vacations and leave the running of the service to me, I began to realize I was in training for what he was—a male madam. In fact, I would have stayed in New York longer had Phillip not sat down with me one day and said, "Grant, I think it's time for you to strike out on your own—open your own service, you'll be the best in the business."

I was nervous that first morning, but his honest manner and intelligence and wit certainly put me at ease. "You can start out at top money if you're as good in bed as I think you are," he said, drinking coffee. "You sure as hell are beautiful."

"You should have seen me when I was seventeen," I said.

And he replied, "Shit, you don't look a day over eighteen, and I aim to keep you that way. I'm not running a chicken factory, though I have a few fourteen-year-olds out there ready and waiting when a customer wants a change of pace, but I don't like my boys looking like old men either."

And then the phone rang and he reached to grab it on the second ring. He was fast and talked to his customers as though each one were his best friend in the world. I got up from the table and looked out over the city, the water. There was such a feeling of class about the brand-new apartment, the fine furniture, the all-glass wall with a view of New York most post cards could not match. I wondered how much business he did there in the apartment. There were no boys running around the place (which was quite different from the constant flow of traffic in Helen's halls) and there seemed to be only three or four bedrooms in the apartment.

When Phillips finished his conversation, I asked him about that. He smiled and explained a few things to me. First of all, the best houses in New York, large or small, had been busted often in the past three years. Many of the madams decided to set up shop in three or four places, running all the business out of one apartment, but using the place only for private parties and special clients. The madam would keep an apartment full of girls in a brownstone in the East Sixties, another in the Village, perhaps one in East Hampton. Phones would be the means of communication, rather than running down the hall or pressing a buzzer. Times were changing, and so were the whorehouses.

Phillip handled a stud farm, boys only, but his customers were of both sexes, and he found out it was easier to keep the two separated. Thus, he had been running two establishments, one for the men, the larger of the two, and one for the women. But, by all standards, the flow of traffic in and out of these houses put the police on the alert, and with the current "cleaning up" of the New York City Police Department, Phillip could put off another bust only so long. Money, freebie blow jobs, favors, they could extend your credit with the cops only so far—then they dragged you off to jail. "It doesn't mean much, and you're out the next morning. But the whole thing is such a fucking hassle, a goddamned nuisance. And a fortune in legal fees."

So, when both of his houses had been busted on the same night, he had decided to spread things over the

141

city and not run "houses" as such. It was the beginning of the kind of stud service I now run, where there is no house where the customers come to meet their boys. Instead, the deal is set and the customer and his boy meet in a hotel, the boy's own apartment, the man's house, wherever. Sometimes I arrange for a man from New Jersey to meet one of my boys in the lobby of the Hotel Americana in Puerto Rico. What is amazing is that the man is in New Jersey, the boy he wants is in Dallas, and I am arranging their meeting in San Juan while sitting in my Chicago apartment.

Phillip also explained that there was less friction involved with the kind of arrangement he had going. There were fewer arguments and less bickering between boys since they no longer lived together. The boys who serviced both men and women had it easier because they could keep that secret from the customers who would stop seeing them if they knew they were fooling around with the other sex. And there is something about having an all-male house which isn't very "male." The origin of a whorehouse comes from females and will always be primarily a feminine institution. Yes, a queen of Russia once kept a stable of boys for her services, it has been around for a long, long time. But there is something to be said about the fact that the house of prostitution has female overtones, whether it is filled with boys or whether it is filled with girls. The men who want boys, and will pay good money for them, want just that: *boys*. The whole point of their giving their money to make love to another male is that they do not want a woman. Thus, is it not better that the atmosphere in which a customer is satisfied is one more suited to men than to women? There is a kind of independent quality we expect in the male sex, and a stud seems less a stud if he lies on a bed in a room of a lovely house filled with other boys in other such rooms. There is something disturbing to male clients about that atmosphere, and it is better business to give them *masculinity* in as many ways as you can. True, some male clients want soft, feminine boys, and you must always have a few on hand. But most want a stud, a man, a hustler. Putting the hustler in the

142

midst of feminine trappings makes him less than a hustler in the customer's eyes. And I think the boys like it better too, in the long run, for if you run the right kind of business and meet with them often and extend the kind of maternal/paternal (for you are both to them) warmth, the feeling of friendship and harmony which was so infectious at Helen's will remain. And it will be your biggest asset.

So Phillip had his boys in apartments all over town. Some lived alone, as they chose. Some shared apartments, and, in one case, six of them lived together. A few of his boys even lived at home with their parents. And, in one amazing case which I have never seen repeated, the boy lived with his mother, who was one of the best independent hookers in town, and she had urged him into the business. Not your run-of-the-mill mother-son relationship, is it?

Anyway, Phillip wanted to see how I performed, and after talking awhile longer, he asked a good-looking guy who had been sitting in the den, going over the books, to answer the phones for an hour or so. "Grant, meet Brian." I smiled and said hello. Later, I was astonished to find out that Brian was Phillip's lover, and had been so for four years. And, even more astonishing, Brian had been completely faithful to Phillip from the day they'd met. I guess it made for a good relationship, because I grew to learn they were very happy together. And you show me an unhappy madam, and I'll show you a fucked-up house.

Phillip and I went to a bedroom where he undressed me and said, "Well, I think I could pull a hundred bucks just to let them have a look at you." I liked that. And I liked what he said when we finished. "Grant, you're terrific!"

You should talk, I thought. It had been a long time since I had really made love to a man. Tricking through Europe had been a lot of blow jobs and fast fucking, and though I had had some tricks which I had wanted to spend days with (men and women), it never happened that way. But now, with Phillip, we were in no hurry, and we explored every inch of each other's bodies, and used

143

all the techniques we knew to give each other pleasure. We sucked each other's cocks and balls, rimmed each other, kissed and rolled over and over on the big bed. We came into each other's mouths at exactly the same moment, and then we kissed again and tasted each other's semen in our mouths. Then he asked if he could fuck me.

And I shivered. That was the moment I had dreaded. I knew that if I were to be a good call boy, I should let men who wanted to fuck me in the ass do so, but I had experienced so much pain in the past, experimenting with it, that I was rather scared. On top of that, Phillip was enormously endowed (eleven inches), and I feared he would split me in two. "Don't be scared," he said.

"You're so big." I remembered the time Flo had tried to stick a nine-inch dildo up my ass. It wouldn't work and I walked around bow-legged for a week. I was very tight.

"Size doesn't matter. How do you think some of the best girls take their twelve-inch boyfriends up the ass? They merely relax their muscles enough and it's no longer painful."

"Re-really?" I asked as he squirted a lubricating jelly between my buttocks.

"Grant, trust me, I know what I'm talking about. I'll let you do it to me too. You've got to be versatile, and it's good that you're tight, but you can't freeze up if a customer wants to screw you." He was right. So I trusted him and tried my best to relax. Each time I tightened up, he ran his hands over my shoulders, massaging them, through my hair, telling me to relax, and soon I learned that he had been right—I was able to take every bit of him and the pain soon was overcome by pleasure. We even tried three different positions before he reached an orgasm. And I thought I knew everything there was to know about sex! Even today I sometimes think there will be a person who will still teach me something new, or one of my boys will tell me something I had never even dreamed of—but that is unlikely, since in the past six months I have not heard a story I haven't heard before.

(The last incident which astonished me and was new to my experience happened six months ago, when I had been up to the cabin (the A-frame) near Aspen with a few of my favorite boys. Billy, one of the most popular, was in the loft with a man and the man's boyfriend. I was downstairs, in the bedroom there, fucking the man's wife. In the middle of it, Billy came to the door, which was unusual and forbidden, and begged me to come out for a moment. I did, good and mad, asking what the hell was wrong. Did he want to lose the three hundred we were getting for the few hours of work? He told me something had happened, and I could see there was pain in his eyes. We went into the kitchen and I discovered what the problem was. He had been standing up while the husband sucked his cock and the boyfriend rimmed him at the same time. Soon he felt the boy pulling on the hair of his ass, hard. He tried to suffer through it, but soon he had to ask the kid to stop because it felt as though all the hair was being bitten out of his ass. Then the kid admitted what had happened—he had been chewing bubble gum, of all goddamned things, and the wad of gum had become entangled in the hair of Billy's ass. And I had to cut it out of him with a pair of scissors as we stood there in the kitchen, laughing like two schoolboys. That's the first time I've ever heard of someone getting bubble gum stuck in their ass!)

Well, I fucked Phillip, and I guess I performed admirably, because he kept complimenting me all afternoon. My first job was that night, and he asked me if I was sure I could manage it. I assured him I could get it up another five times that day. And I could have, I was so hot to get going and become the top hustler in New York City!

The job turned out to be an easy one, an almost boring one, come to think of it. The guy I met at the New York Hilton used Phillip's service whenever he was in New York, but he never wanted the same boy twice, which was unusual—most men have their favorites and ask for them again and again. So I was new and he dug me.

There was a small projector set up on a table, and

after I had shed my clothes and he had done the same, he turned out the light and clicked on the projector. And a movie appeared on the wall, a film of two beautiful women making love to each other. He was very turned on by it and as he watched it he asked me to beat him off, which I did, and my hands got damn tired because he held off shooting till the damn thing finished. I swear, he came just as the girls jumped into a bathtub together and giggled their way into cleansing each other after going through just about everything a woman could do with another female. As the words *the end* appeared on the screen, the guy hit, and I let out a deep breath and finally gave my hands a rest.

He sucked me off right after that and I left.

I arrived back at Phillip's before midnight because I was going to stay there till Phillip decided just where to put me—alone or with some other guys. Since I could dig having women customers, he had to be careful which boys, if any, he would have me live with. It turned out that he had already made up his mind when I came back to the apartment. "You belong in the Village," he said, "because you have that hunky, casual look that so many guys want. You belong in jeans and casual clothes, that's your *look*." (Hmmm. My *look* was a year or so ahead of its time, because the casual denim trend is certainly the look of today.)

So Phillip told me he was going to get me a nice place in the Village, which was very popular at that time, meaning customers liked knowing their boy came from the Village, and that I would live alone.

I liked that.

I had a few different apartments while I worked New York, but none was as nice and comfortable as the place Phillip found for me on Christopher Street. A small living room with a fireplace, a tiny kitchen, a perfect-size bedroom. Phillip advanced me a good chunk of money so I could buy some clothes and fill up the big closet. Soon I had an outfit for the streets, another for the opera, another for weekends on Fire Island, warm clothes for New England vacations, when I would travel to spend a few

146

days with a trick while her husband was on a business trip, or when his wife was off visiting her mother.

I came to know some of the kids living around there, straight, gay, in between, and I soon discovered little out-of-the-way restaurants and coffee houses where I would go after finishing with a customer.

Phillip provided me with everything I needed, and I mean beyond clothing and rent and food. If a certain customer was into bondage, he would send over a suitcase with the necessary tools for the night—ropes, whips, black gloves, whatever was required. I had one woman, a very rich Jewess who belonged to one of the biggest banking families in the city, who often had me dress up as a Nazi general, but letting my cock hang from my leather pants. She would ask to be bound to the bed, naked, and whipped on her thighs and breasts while being told she was going to go to the gas chambers. It was her thing, she paid well, and I never questioned her need to be humiliated. Phillip told me once that she mentioned that Tracy was her favorite general because of his light hair (I guess I could easily pass for German) and big cock (didn't she ever notice I was circumcised?).

I learned a lot about kinky sex, more so than I had experienced in California. There was the opera tenor who would jerk me off into a dish of chocolate ice cream before he ate it. I once made a terrible mistake by changing flavors on him. I think I bought butter pecan in place of chocolate and he went into a fit. Phillip reminded me, within an hour, that the customer is always right.

I haven't forgotten since.

I would regularly attend the theater on the arm of a matron of New York society, and twice I made the newspapers as we were emerging from a limousine to attend a gala opening of a Broadway play. I sometimes look at the photographs from the papers, because she was a handsome woman and I looked damn good standing next to her in my tux and all, watching the photographers snap all around us. I had come quite a way from the day the creepy little producer in Malibu snapped photos of me taking a leak. What the papers and patrons of the arts did not know about the famous matron was that she sucked my cock in the back of the limousine on the way *to* the theater, and again on the way *from* the theater. When she was smiling as she emerged from the long sleek Cadillac, it was not a put-on for the cameras. She had just had a good shot of hot jism pushed down her throat, and she loved it. Her chauffeur should write a book about her, now that she's dead. Boy, the stories he could tell! And, you know, she gave a damn good blow job, as long as her false teeth were fastened properly.

I remember the "cowboy" very well. He was a hunky dude from Oklahoma who called me his young stallion and sat on my ass as I pretended to be a horse he was attempting to tame. I ended up, each time, taming him by shoving my cock up his ass.

There was an old man who wanted nothing more than to watch me shower. He never took his clothes off, never played with himself through his pants, never touched me. He merely watched with a very satisfied expression on his face.

There was a woman, and quite a beautiful one, who would have me stand on a step ladder (provided by Phillip) over the bathtub. She would lie in the tub and spread her legs, and then open her pussy with her hands. And then I would piss on her pussy, or *into* it, I should say, from high on the ladder.

There was the artist and his wife who would smear paint all over my body and have me roll around on a chunk of canvas. I often wondered what they did with those creations. I would bet that some of them are hanging in living rooms in Manhattan today.

A woman once made a plaster cast of my cock, which really fascinated me because this was before the rock-star groupies and the plaster casters became popular. Once that whole scene got going, I found out the woman had been making casts of guys' dicks for years, and not only hustlers—some pretty famous names. Once when I visited her in her studio, she showed me some of the cock sculptures she had, and I was pretty stunned when I saw the names on the labels under them. I really felt good the day she told me she liked my cock better than Mick Jagger's.

There was the retired movie star who would have me recite portions of *Hamlet* for her while she sucked my dick. There was the man who was an ambassador to the United States from one of the European countries who would reserve a room for me at the Plaza Hotel, and then he would arrive, after I had already arrived and taken off my clothes, and pretend to be in the wrong room, and I would have to coax him into staying. I could read any scenario and do a damn good job of acting because I had a ball doing what I was doing.

But sex wasn't my life, it was my job, and although it took up most of my time and I enjoyed every minute of it, I had another life as well. I started to write. Yes, I'll never forget that Eleanor gave me that copy of *Tender Is the Night*, and that Shelley called me her Youngblood Hawke, and that Helen had encouraged me to read through her entire library, *including* Gertrude Stein, whom I now love. I didn't know if I could write more than my name, but there was a way to find out—sit my ass down and try. I bought a portable typewriter and in three months I emerged with a book. It was a sex book, because that is what I know best, and I figured a young novelist should write about his own experience, but, nevertheless, it was terrible. I mean, it was a real piece of shit. But I took the chance of sending it to a small porno publisher and he bought it for three hundred dollars. I was the happiest guy in the world, and I ran out and spent the entire amount on an *electric* typewriter!

Knowing the book was for shit did me good, because if I had been stupid enough to convince myself it was worth anything, I would have been in trouble. I saw what was wrong with it (the only good parts were the sex scenes; the story stank and the characters were cardboard) and I decided in the next one I would do better.

And I did, but not by a lot. I worked at the second one for a whole year, really worked at it. Granted, I didn't have much time to spend on it, but when I did, I worked painstakingly. I had the good luck to sell the second one to a publisher in California who took the time to tell me what was wrong with the book and what I could do to make my next one better. And I sold the third one just last year. The money meant nothing because I could make as much money in four hours as I got for all of them put together, but the practice is wonderful, and the feeling of pride that I might have set down at least a few good paragraphs in the middle of all those sex scenes and crazy characters is overwhelming. I put the fourth one aside to write this book, and I only hope this is an improvement over the third. I think it has to be, because this is not a novel, it is a remembrance, a true story, and it seems to be flowing better than anything I've ever written. I don't know if it will read that way, but that's how it seems to be coming out of me.

Phillip and Brian found my desire to write the great American novel amusing. They took to calling me Hemingway when we were having dinner together, or when we were spending an afternoon on the beach in Miami in the winter.

"Hey, Hemingway," Phillip would say, "wanna go to Florida and get your ass tanned?" And then he would tell me the name of the airline, the flight number, and the hotel where I was to meet them in Miami. Many of our customers, especially the Jews, spent the winter in sunny, humid, buggy Florida, and so we followed.

We had good times together, seeing movies, going to parties, going deep-sea fishing (that's when they really ribbed me about being Hemingway!), getting to know new people. But all the time I was studying Phillip's way of handling things, his way of handling business. He taught me how to keep books and what to do in emergencies— like where to hide them when the cops were rapping at the door (the vegetable drawer of the refrigerator was his favorite spot). When we were in New York, I began to spend more time at United Nations Plaza than at my apartment because I was so eager to help out on the business end of the business. Whenever Phillip would entertain special customers or throw a party, I would be one of the boys who would participate, and I would often spend the night at the home-base (as we called it) apartment and would let Phillip and Brian sleep late into the morning, because I would be up early, answering the phone, making appointments I was allowed to make. I was taking in as much as I could, and I knew it was going to pay off.

I really got an education about drugs through Phillip. He made me realize that drug use was growing and there was a place for it—but not in a brothel. Phillip would tolerate the use of poppers (amyl nitrate) and grass, for they often helped in pleasing the customer, and if the customer was on uppers or downers it made no difference to Phillip. I found out most women I slept with were hooked on diet pills. But Phillip would not provide the customers with reds and whites, just as he would not provide a customer with heroin if he had asked for it. If a customer wanted to sniff coke while having sex, then that was his pleasure, and as long as he didn't force the boy he was with into sharing it, Phillip didn't mind. But if Phillip found out one of his boys had been forced to "trip" with a customer or experiment with drugs he considered dangerous, that was the last time that customer would visit us.

Phillip and Brian smoked a good deal of marijuana, which I had already become used to in California—I told you everything happens first in California. I have found it fun at times, especially when I smoke it socially, at a party, before a group of us have sex. It is at those times that it seems to work best for me, because everyone becomes very loose and free, sometimes giggly and silly, but that too can be exciting—I like to have a good time when I'm fucking, and especially when I'm involved in an orgy.

But I can take or leave grass at all other times, just as I can take or leave booze (I usually leave both). I honestly like to feel a natural high, the high that requires no artificial stimulation, the high I feel when I'm having a very good sexual trip with someone. Since I have been able to find this very satisfying level of consciousness, I don't find drugs or liquor necessary. I always keep liquor, grass, and poppers in my house, and make sure my boys are supplied with all three. But as for my own personal use, I'd rather read a book.

I moved three times in New York. The first time because if I hadn't I would have ended up in rubble—they tore down my building. I hated to leave that wonderful little apartment in the Village, and seeing that I was being forced out, I decided I wanted to live somewhere new, in a part of the city I didn't know as well. So Phillip found me a brand-new apartment, all glass and steel, near Lincoln Center.

I hated it. It was cold and sterile, no matter what we did to try to disguise it, and I could tell the customers were as unhappy there as I was. Everyone had loved the warmth of my living room lined with books, the fireplace casting a golden glow over the room, the leather chairs. There is something to be said about atmosphere—and the second place had none.

So the third place was in the East Seventies, not far from Central Park, which I liked because I got myself a little dog and we took a long walk through the park each morning at dawn (when I could get up that early—often, to tell the truth, I was going to bed at that hour!). My little dog's name was Pepper because he was a black-and-brown-and-white spotted mutt, and I loved him.

And, like so many people in my life, he up and disappeared one day. I like to think he decided to go out and hustle on his own, and that he had a good time.

I learned what it was like to be "known" to many people in the city, people you would normally have to deal with in everyday life, but being a hustler and belonging to the best stud-farm in the city, things were a little different. A doctor, much like the doctor who checked out Helen's brood all the time, made us feel as if we were his favorite patients, and even at the slightest sign of a cold we could walk into his office without an appointment and get in to see him. I think Phillip provided the man or his wife (I don't think the guy was gay) with freebies anytime it was asked, though I was never one of them. Phillip took good medical care of his boys, because a sick hustler is no hustler at all.

152

The third building I lived in had a doorman, and he would get a nice tip every week for being so kind to my visitors. The woman across the hall once invited a customer in for coffee when I had become caught in a jam in the subway at rush hour; I paid her by giving her a freebie fuck when her husband went to work the next day. And from then on she brought my mail upstairs and did all kinds of favors for me. All for a fast screw now and then.

When I first started working for Phillip, I would accompany Brian on many errands. We visited the liquor man who tossed in an extra case of scotch, saying to Brian, "Tell Delaney last night's was the best ever!" When we picked up two new suits Phillip had ordered for one of the boys from his tailor, the man tossed in a Cardin scarf for Phillip. I knew that he too was being paid in boys and not money. Often the manager of the hotel in which we were staying would tell us, "It's on the house." And not only rooms; meals and drinks and use of the pool on the roof were free also. The decorator who tried (but didn't succeed) to fix up my second apartment settled for a blow job as payment. And, soon after I had moved into the third apartment, I realized I was being sent a very ugly man (which was odd; Phillip always sent me the best) because of the fact that he worked for the telephone company and was "reworking" Phillip's bill each month.

It is amazing what money will buy. But it is even more amazing what a little sex will buy! I swear we could do away with the inflation we're fighting today by paying for things with our bodies and not money. The value of the dollar keeps fluctuating, but the value of a good stiff cock doesn't change.

I have paid for airline tickets with my cock. I have taught one boy to finance an entire college education with his tight ass. Instead of talking one of the senior officers of a large Chicago bank into giving me a sizable loan, I fucked her into it. My eight inches has paid for prescriptions, laundry and dry cleaning, ski equipment, stationery, and radial tires.

I've often wondered if a person can pay their income

153

tax with sex. I rather doubt it; you gotta draw the line somewhere.

I sometimes found it very hypocritical that we would be servicing members of the government, city, state, and country, high-ranking officers of the police force, detectives, you name it, and these are the people who must often be paid off, these are the very people who refuse to let you alone. They say they are just "doing their job." But isn't that exactly what *we* are doing? Do we harass *them*?

I hate double standards. For example, one of my clients when I first moved back to Chicago was a man I had met in New York, when he was in town for a booksellers' convention. He owned (and still owns) a large religious-book publishing house in the Midwest. He prints Bibles and all kinds of highly moralistic literature, and he is well regarded in his profession, and in the last year has become somewhat of a pop moralist spokesman for a group of quasi-educators and religious leaders who have backed the Supreme Court's pornography ruling. He has been on television and in the papers, constantly spouting what a "corrupting influence" pornography has had on the "moral fiber" of our country. I wish I had taken a photograph the day he had me stick a golf club up his ass.

I am very much opposed to censorship of any kind, to oppression of freedom of any kind. I'll never forget the day Phillip called me into the den and told me he had talked to Helen. I was excited to hear what was happening in Chicago, but his mood seemed so somber. "What's wrong?" I asked.

"Helen was raided and closed down. Permanently, it seems." He went on to tell me that a few changes in the set-up of officials in the Cook County Sheriff's Department had caused the heat to be put on the house.

"But that happens all the time," I said, knowing enough about raids to know they didn't mean much other than the time and money wasted.

"You're smart, Hemingway," Phillip said. Then he told me the truth. It seemed that the property on which Helen's house stood was wanted by a high rise develop-

ment company, which was coincidentally owned
brother of the cousin of the mayor's friend or son
like that, and the raid had been used to get the
closed down, not for moral reasons, but for po...cal
reasons, which are always money reasons. It turned out
that the high-rise company did not get Helen's land for
four more years because the neighbors all fought hard,
but Helen did indeed give up the kind of house she had
once run, and turned to working with a few girls in an
apartment on Lake Shore Drive. I was sorry to hear
that it had happened.

"Grant, I'm going to have to tell you something you're
not going to like hearing, and I'm really sorry about it."

I stared at him. I couldn't imagine what it could be.

"Miss Pearl, your friend at Helen's, died right after
the raid. It seems the cops busted up the place pretty
bad and she tried to help Helen hide the books when,
Helen says, a fucking cop shoved Pearl away. It seems
she lost her balance and nearly fell out of a second-story
window. She was so scared she suffered a heart attack.
She died quietly at the hosupital, and an intern later told
Helen that she had mentioned Tracy and Lacey before
she passed away."

I got up and walked around the room a few times
and then asked Phillip if I could get out of the meeting I
had with a john that night. It was one of the few days
when I knew nothing in the world could make me get
it up.

Hustlers are human too.

As I walked along the boardwalk in the rain in Atlantic
City (that's where I went as soon as I'd left Phillip's)
that night, I kept myself together enough to make a
determined effort, when I had a place of my own, or a
service of my own, to fight raids and cops and hypocritical bastards who were our "elected officials" and
paid for our services by night, but during the day did
their best to ruin us. I thought about Shelley and about
the fact that I had sold a book, even though it was
garbage. Somehow now it seemed my lies to her had
not been lies at all, but premature truth. I relieved

myself of some of the guilt I had been carrying on my shoulders for having hurt her so. I still loved her, and I knew I always would. But it didn't hurt quite so much to think of her now, and that was good.

I was glad I had known a woman so full of life as Pearl. I was glad I had saved her letters and hoped that one day I could use them to tell the story of her life, which is a lot more fascinating than the life of any madam I have ever heard. It is one thing to work your way up to the top in the field of prostitution; it is quite another to start as the daughter of a slave and work your way through the white whorehouses of the South, to become the cook in what was Chicago's best modern-day brothel. I don't know exactly how old Miss Pearl was when she died (I would not doubt that she was pushing a hundred), but a lot of people loved her and would miss her. I often thought that that was one of the reasons Helen had decided not to fight any longer—she didn't have Pearl with her, and it would never have been the same.

I called Kent that night, from Atlantic City. He was going to college (which he didn't like all that much) in Minneapolis at the time and was glad to hear from me. He said, "When the hell are you going to come back here? The Midwest isn't the same without you."

"Soon," I promised, "soon."

And, a month later, after dinner one night, Brian smiled while Phillip told me he thought I was ready to become a madam myself.

Then, for the first and last time in my life, I did a little "camping." I jumped up, threw my hands up and out as though I were on stage and a big hot klieg light had just found my face. Then, doing what I could to muster up a Fanny Brice-Barbra Streisand voice, I yelled, "ME, A MADAM?" and fell back against the wall.

Phillip and Brian cracked up.

It was the easiest goodbye I ever had to say. I had been careful while in New York not to make such close friends that I could not bear leaving them; thus all my friendships were casual ones, and though I would miss some of the people, the thought of not seeing them again was easy to live with. I knew I was taking a nice list of phone numbers, which Phillip had provided, phone numbers that would start business rolling. I would miss Phillip and Brian, but I knew I would see them often, and besides, I wasn't really leaving anything, I was going on to something better. And they were the guys who had helped me to do it.

I arrived in Chicago shortly after 1972 began, but in quite a different fashion from the day I'd stepped off the train from Milwaukee with only a suitcase and a copy of *Tender Is the Night* in hand. This time I held my head high, without any pangs of insecurity. In fact, I felt as though I had arrived home.

To top it off, it was snowing.

CHAPTER SIX

The Pleasure Is All Mine

Chicago, I do admit, is "my kind of town."

Though I hate it in January, I loved it when I drove up Michigan Avenue in a cab, on my way to Helen's. That was one January when the snow and sleet and angry drivers and the bundling-up you have to do to face the weather were worth it. I had come full circle, and inside me was all the hope in the world.

Helen actually had tears in her eyes when she saw me, and Lacey acted as though her little brother had returned from the war. Only Miss Pearl was missing, but the letters in my suitcase, those wonderful letters which formed a chronicle of her life and times, they were with me, and as long as they would be, so would her spirit.

As long as I mentioned Miss Pearl, let me tell you two things. First, I wept inside me when I watched *The Autobiography of Miss Jane Pittman* on television. I cried for Miss Jane and for Miss Pearl and I decided then that one day, perhaps this year, maybe when I'm old and gray, I'll take those letters I treasure so much and compile them into the life story of a woman as remarkable as the now-unforgettable Miss Jane.

Second, when Flora, the customer who is the slave to my "Northern soldier," first asked me to enact such a scenario, I almost refused—and I never refuse a request. But because Florabelle is black and because she is shaped much like Pearl, I didn't think I could do it. I got my shit together mighty fast, however, while she explained that

158

her husband, Harvard, had tried it with her but because he was black he didn't play the part of a bluecoat very well. I found that amusing and I knew that Pearl would understand—she understood well what games were played in whorehouses, and she herself would probably get a good chuckle out of the scene.

Pearl. Helen. Lacey. Chicago. We talked on and on, reminiscing. I met Helen's new lover, Cindy, a pretty young hopeful actress whom Helen was keeping. She was perky and fun and she was amazed that I was going to start a service of my own. "You're so young!" she said.

Helen shook her head. "This guy's been around, honey, he's seen the asshole of the world, inside out, and he's crawled out into the sunshine, yes he has! Hell, anyone who likes Stein can't be all bad!"

I'd written to her each time I had finished another Gertrude Stein book, or books about her, to thank her for first getting me interested.

"So, baby, you're gonna become Chicago's Phil Delaney, huh?" she asked, the rings still on her fingers. Though she looked the same, small, fat, queenly sitting in her big red chair with a footstool in front of her, I could tell the drive had gone out of her and she was near to retiring. "It's a hard life, Tracy, a hard life. But the business needs a kid like you. I think . . . naw, I'll *bet* my ass you make it!" And she had quite an ass to bet.

So I rented an apartment for the time being, near Old Town, near the house I had begun my career in, and decided I was going to take my time and do things right.

But I had to get nostalgia out of my bones, so the very next day I took a walk down LaSalle Street and stopped in front of the old house. It was still standing, but the life had gone out of it. The paint was chipping and the beautiful gold door knockers I remembered so well were gone. I looked up to the third floor, to my old window, and saw a poster taped to it. And then a beautiful blond boy walked by me and up the stairs and pulled out a key. "Excuse me," I said.

He looked down at me on the sidewalk and smiled. "Hi."

"Hello. Do you live here?"

He nodded. "Yeah, I'm one of them."

"I used to live here, quite a few years ago."

He looked puzzled. "It had to be *quite* a few years ago. We just moved in last month, and up until a year or so ago this was a famous—"

"—whorehouse." I beat him to it.

He looked surprised that I knew. "We get a lot of guys coming around, still looking for the place, but I didn't think anyone as young—"

I cut him off again. "Hey, listen, would you care if I . . . well, if I came in for a minute, just to see . . ."

"Sure, come on in."

And I did. Within an hour I was sitting on the living room floor drinking apple juice with the kids who lived there. David, the blond boy I had met outside, and Lee, June, and Tom, and their cat, and a girl named Judy who had the room I once made money in. They told me how rundown the place had been when they'd moved in; it had been standing vacant since the raid. The landlord warned them the place could be torn down any day, to make way for the high rise, but if they wanted to stay as long as the neighbors could fight off the wreckers, they were welcome to it. They had done a good job fixing it up, and the piano bar was still where I remembered it and Miss Pearl's kitchen hadn't changed a bit, except that the smell of pecan pie was gone.

Then I explained my connection with the place and they found it hard to believe at first, but became so entranced with my tales about life in the famous whorehouse that they never wanted me to leave. It was a good afternoon, I had liked meeting them and wished them well in their new and historical home, and left wishing that Paul, wherever he was, could have been with me. He would have loved it.

And so I set out to find boys. You don't run a stud service without studs, and I wanted the best. Phillip had the names of a few he felt were worth looking up, but one turned out to be too old. I wanted young, hunky, masculine guys. Helen recommended a few that Joey DeFranco had not had his dirty hands on, and they turned

160

out to be terrific. I know, because just as Phillip "auditioned" me, I did the same with my prospective boys.

I didn't search out the bathrooms of the bus station and I didn't comb back rows of movie theaters. I watched the streets in the good sections of town, keeping an eye for the boy who showed promise, the kind of boy who looks attractive, seems together enough to handle himself, and likes money. You can read it on a face, in the eyes. They're not hard to find. And the ones I found, in turn, found me others.

Within three months, as the snows of winter turned to the rainy days of spring, I had a good stable of studs and we were ready to go.

Where did we go?

To jail.

My mistake was to have stayed in the Old Town area for so long. I didn't know Chicago all that well, geographically that is—cities change and different areas within each city take on new appearances and new reputations. The Old Town area in 1972 was a haven for the suburban hippies, the kids who pulled into town on Saturday and Sunday nights in their parents' big autos, ready to have a good time. It was a tourist attraction, or at least Wells Street was, the major street, lined with head shops and restaurants and boutiques and the like. Consequently, the place and all surrounding streets were well watched by the Chicago police force, whom I never did have any use for. After the Democratic Convention of 1968, or what I had read about it, I began to *hate* the Chicago cops. Then, topping everything off, the way Miss Pearl met her death . . .

So the last thing I wanted was a raid, especially before I even got started. I was fighting mad.

I had put down a deposit on an apartment near the lake, farther north, a beautiful place where I would run my business, very much like the set-up Phillip had. I'd come to feel close to two boys, Billy and Rob, and I trusted them and asked them to live in the place with me. I had known Rob from Miami, where he often worked ın the winter, and he had promised to come and join me whenever I started my own place.

Thing about it was, I didn't want to start a "place," I wasn't planning on running a house. I had already set up boys in apartments all around the city, even as far north as Milwaukee, and had, the day before the raid, sent two of them to Los Angeles to work things there. I wanted to start out big, and starting on the national level is about as big as you can begin. But I didn't count on the police.

Especially that night, because we had not even expected to be turning tricks. Billy, Rob, and I had gone to the new place and talked with a decorator who was fixing it up (though he was a screaming queen, he was turning the place into a very masculine and comfortable haven). Billy gave him a freebie fuck in one of the bedrooms (I told you sex can pay for anything) while Rob and I watched the phone man installing the thousands of wires and connections which would bring us thousands of calls and many thousands of dollars.

After the decorator and the telephone man left, we went out for something to eat, stopping at the McDonald's on Clark Street, of all places, and we decided on the spur of the moment to have a little party that night since we were all in good spirits. Before we went home, I stopped at the liquor store where I had come to know the proprietor quite well (I had fucked his wife while he filmed it and now I got all the booze I wanted that way) and picked up some wine, and then Billy made a stop on North Avenue to get some grass. It was a kind of celebration because we would begin to move into the new apartment the next day, and the four other boys who were still living with us in Old Town would be splitting into twosomes and taking their own places. So we popped popcorn, opened the wine, smoked some grass, all seven of us, and then the doorbell rang.

It was a guy I remembered from New York and he had two friends with him, a man and a woman, and could they come in, was I taking customers? I really didn't know what to tell them, but of course I asked them in. Seems they were already a bit loaded themselves and had

162

forgotten to park their rented car in a parking place. Yes, they just stopped in the middle of the street, the dumb assholes, and had let it sit there. I guess they were so excited about finding the address, not one of them remembered they had left the car in the middle of the road!

Well, they loved the group scene, and after they had plunked down a hundred bucks we all got undressed and began having a wonderful sucking and fucking party on the living room floor. The girl the man had brought with him was an insatiable cocksucker, and she was doing us guys two at a time while the other dude who had come with them fucked her dog-style. We were having one hell of a party when the bell rang again.

Everyone froze, but soon they started giggling because we were feeling pretty crazy by that time—everyone but me and Rob. Neither of us get too stoned on grass, and we don't care to drink all that much.

I slid into my jeans and went into the little foyer and opened the sliding window in the door. It was a handsome man in his forties. "Grant?" he asked.

"Yeah, who are you?" I replied.

"I'm with the others."

"Wait a minute," I said, and went back into the living room. None of them were in any condition to be coherent. I mean, guys were coming and the girl was squealing and I tried asking them if they had been expecting someone else. "Did someone park the car?" I asked, knowing what a bitch it was to find parking on a Friday night in that area. I thought maybe the guy at the door had driven around to find a space and then walked to the apartment.

"Sure," was the reply from the guy I'd known from New York. *Of course someone parked the car*, he must have thought.

Shit. I wasn't even thinking about cops because I wasn't running a house, you know? How did I know there was a sheet of paper in the front seat of the car (which was by that time causing one hell of a traffic jam) which had my name, address, and phone number on it?

163

How did I know the fuzz had been watching me like a hawk for weeks?

I opened the little window again and this time the man flashed a fifty-dollar bill in front of it. "Come on, man, I'm getting horny!" he said, and if that isn't entrapment, I don't know what is. So I opened the door and just as I did the girl, naked as the day she was born, came into the foyer and said, "Hey, let me suck you, too!" She fell to her knees in front of me before I could tell the guy to take his coat off, but before I had a chance to speak, while she was pulling down my zipper, I saw a badge flash in my face and suddenly something like five plainclothesmen burst into the place. And, following them came—as though Bonnie and Clyde were hiding out in the apartment—three cops in uniform.

Well, things were pretty hectic there for a little while. There were no books yet, but I did have listings of potential customers, listings of boys who would be working for us, things I certainly would not want those fucking pigs to get their hands on. There was much commotion, and thank God for that dumb girl—she didn't even know we were being raided, she was so drunk and so hungry for another cock. She grabbed one of the uniformed cops and yanked his zipper down and tried with all her might to get his dick out of his pants! Two of the other pigs pulled her off him and she bit one of them on the leg and then yanked him to the floor and they had one hell of a time trying to get her calmed down and into her clothes. Which was what I needed—time.

Because I was the only person with pants on, they were paying little attention to me. When the chick bit the guy's leg I bolted into the kitchen and grabbed the black book which listed all the customers and boys working for me and shoved it under the vegetable drawer in the refrigerator. Thank God for Phillip Delaney. I would have stuck it in with the lettuce and carrots and mushrooms, but there wasn't a vegetable in the drawer. So I figured *under* it would be even safer. "What the fuck're you doin'?" a pig asked as I was closing the refrigerator.

"I wanted to make a sandwich before we go to jail,

something to eat on the way," I said, and he shoved me across the room and told me to get my shoes and a shirt on. The idiot was stupid enough not to wonder what the hell I had really been doing in the refrigerator.

Well, I found out later that Rob had been equally fast. He had taken the grass and flushed it down the toilet the moment he'd heard them charge into the foyer. The girl kneeling in front of me had slowed them up, because the first cop had to take a good look at her tits and cunt, so they all piled on top of each other before they got into the living room, where they found the guys. "Lookit this!" one of the pigs shouted. "A fag party!"

I decided not to wear any shoes, for the hell of it, and Billy could only find his jockey shorts and not his pants so they hustled him into the wagon just like that, almost naked. The neighbors were having a field day, counting the number of boys they were dragging out of the place; they freaked out over seeing only one girl being hustled into the police van with us. I'm surprised the cops didn't take her separately, but I guess they figured we were all alike: sick.

Inside the wagon, I told the boys not to worry. I had grabbed the money I kept in the cookie jar (honest, that's where I stashed the cash) and it was in my pocket. A big creep of a cop sat back there with us, holding some things they'd brought along which turned out, to their surprise, to be nothing more than a scrapbook full of photos (none of them pornographic, thank God) and Pearl's letters (which I retrieved and the next day put in a safe-deposit box) and some of my writing (no loss if I don't get that back, I thought). The girl giggled her way to the station, but about halfway there she tried to start sucking cock again, but the big pig warned her not to. Then she tried to put the make on him and he yelled at her, so she ripped off her blouse and exposed her tits and sat across from him for the rest of the trip, driving him crazy as he looked up at her jugs with lustful eyes. "Eat your fucking heart out," she would whisper, playing with her nipples.

Actually it was very amusing.

About halfway to the station, the crazy girl started telling the cop (and us) a story, and I couldn't resist breaking into a fit of laughter. Here was this cop, right, trying to "guard" us while we were being carted off to jail. And here's this horny and very upset chick facing him, naked to the waist, her big brown nipples almost three inches from his nose, bouncing as we rode over Chicago's potholed streets, and he couldn't do anything but *look*! So she said, "I've been in this thing before. You know that?" She looked the pig square in the eye and put her hands on her hips. "Yeah, copper, see, me and the boys here, we could really do a fuckin' number on ya, just like me and the dykes did down at the fuckin' beach."

What the hell was she talking about? All our expressions asked that question, and the cop looked interested too. She continued without any encouragement:

"See, I was at the beach with one of my girlfriends, Mitzi . . . she kinda looks like what's her name, Judy Garland's kid . . ."

"Liza Minnelli," I said.

"Yeah, her. Anyhow, it's this terrific day and me and Mitzi go to the beach and it happens that it's dyke convention day or somethin', I don't know. Mitzi knows a lotta gay girls. So we're passin' around a bottle of wine and talkin' like girls do, you know, right?" She looked at Billy. He nodded (and probably didn't have the foggiest idea what the hell she meant).

"Anyhow," she continued, bouncing up and down as we rounded a corner, "we got to talkin' about how girls got the right to not wear bras and then we started talkin' about topless bathin' suits and all of a sudden Mitzi drops her top to the sand! And Mitzi's got knockers'll crack a fuckin' cement lamppost!"

Her voice reminded me of some movie star. I started thinking it was Jean Harlow, but that wasn't it. Then Goldie Hawn (I think *Laugh-in* was big right around then) but that wasn't it either. *Who the hell does she remind me of?*

"So this big bull thing, she drops her top, and another one did the same, and this little skinny chick, and then I pulled off my top and man, we had the whole beach goin' gaagaa! I swear we caused a couple a fuckin' accidents with those guys drivin' along the Outer Drive."

"Look," the cop suddenly said, "no talking back here."

She lifted her hand as though she was gonna haul off and slap him! "Hey, flatfoot, you want us to do what me and the girls did?"

What the hell *did* she and the girls do?

"In about ten minutes, we're causin' this big commotion, like Mayor Daley died on the beach or somethin'. I mean the whole goddamn police force was coming at us. So they pulled out their sticks . . ." She looked the cop up and down and rubbed her nipples. "I said *sticks,* man, not dicks."

Billy laughed and the cop shot him a sneer.

"So, the pigs load us into one dinky wagon, me and all these bull dykes, a wagon just like this one." She looked around and giggled. "Hell, maybe it was this one!"

"Shut up." The cop was trying his damnedest to keep order, but his eyes were glued to her tits.

"Wanda, she's the big bull bitch, a pal of Mitzi's, she says, 'LOOK, GIRLS, WE GOTTA GET THE FUCKIN' HELL OUTTA HERE!' and she tells us, 'EVERYONE TO ONE SIDE OF THE VAN, COME ON!' See, we were packed in there and the cops were runnin' down the beach tryin' to catch the one girl who escaped. So we listened to big Wanda, and we pressed against one side of the van, and then we ran to the other, and back and forth. We could hear the crowd cheerin' like crazy, cause the whole goddamned thing was rockin' back and forth, back and forth, and Wanda kept saying, 'HARDER, FASTER, WE'RE GONNA DO IT, WE'RE GONNA TIP IT!' and sure enough, the whole goddamned fuckin' pig wagon tipped over on its side and the doors broke open and the cop up front got knocked out and the horn started blowin' and the crowd, man, they were eatin' it up, and we crawled out, about fifteen big hard ladies and me, tits bobbin' everywhere and we ran, man, we ran like we had firecrackers up our asses and those fuckin' pigs couldn't believe it . . . this big strong cage with wheels lyin' there on its side with the horn tootin' like crazy!"

She laughed like crazy, and I did too—we all did. All of us but the cop, who pretended it wasn't funny. But anyone who had any imagination could easily conjure up the image of this carload of dykes and dumb blondes rocking a police wagon back and forth till it toppled and cracked open and the horn went off and a gang of screaming half-naked women went running to their freedom. . . .

"SHUT THE FUCK UP, ALL OF YOU!" the cop shouted, lifting his dick. I mean stick!

"Eat my asshole!" the girl said in reply.

He didn't.

"Okay, everybody, settle down," I said, pretending to be the father of the group, but the truth was I was laughing harder than any of them. I guess I was telling myself to settle down. I figured that cop could get mean if he wanted to, and I doubted if he'd take a whack at the dumb broad with the jugs. I figured he'd like to ram that club he was holding into someone else's body—mine, for instance. So we settled down.

Billy and the other boys were scared, but thank goodness they trusted me, and none of them were underage. I made sure of that when I signed them up, and when men wanted chicken or a woman customer would request a boy underage, I would only arrange it if the price was right (steep) and the client completely reliable. You can get into trouble with youngsters, and though I was one when I began, I don't recommend it. I mean I don't really recommend hustling till you are old enough to take care of yourself legally—people like Joey DeFranco didn't care if they were eleven or seventeen; if the kid could get a hard-on, he would take him. And work him nearly to death. If a kid thirteen wanted to hustle and had his head together with it, fine, but he would have to hustle on the street. I would not take him in under any circumstances, and since the Houston scare and the raids a few years back on Long Island, on the chicken-call-boy operation there, and the very recent homosexual-fuck-film arrests in California which concerned very young boys, I would be too scared to ever get into that.

Anyhow, we got to the station and we must have made a wonderful sight: one girl with her tits hanging out of her mink coat, two men in wrinkled business suits, and seven young guys, one barefoot, and one in his jockey shorts. The police greeted us as the neighbors had—with open mouths. (I think the neighbors thought it was a drug bust; I don't think male prostitution had crossed their innocent minds, God bless 'em.)

I made one call for all of us, or at least for my boys. Helen said, "Tracy, baby, hang on. I'll take care of it fast." I hated calling her, hated having to remind her of what had ruined her house, but I think she was pleased I did, because I heard some of the fight coming back into her voice.

They tried to interrogate us, but they didn't do very well. When they asked the chick her name, she told them, "Mamie Eisenhower." When they asked me what my occupation was, I told them I wrote. "Whaddaya write?" the jerk asked. "Letters to Ann Landers and my congressman," I replied. They soon saw they weren't going to get far.

Someone said, "Let the guys downtown take care of 'em," and with that we were left in this small cell, all of us, including the girl. I guess they didn't have a matron to handle her at the time. So we sat down on the cold floor and two cops "guarded" us, both of them staring at her big tits, while she told us a story to pass the time.

"Listen," she said, and then it came to me—Judy Holliday! That's who she reminded me of! "I gotta tell you fellas about the time I was in Vegas. I was with this really terrific fella, ya know, and he was down shootin' craps all night or somethin' and I got bored so I went out to some goddamn bar or somethin' and when I got back to the hotel he was still at the fuckin' tables. So I got real puffy and told him I was flyin' home the next day and went up to the room and stripped and got in bed."

The cops were listening close by this time.

"So about five in the mornin' he comes up and says—

169

real big-man like, ya know?—'BABY, I DID IT!' I says, 'FUCK YOU' and turned over in bed and all of a sudden he clicks on the light and tosses about twenty thousand smackeroos all over the place, all over me, all over the bed, everywhere!"

"Wow," one of the cops breathed, and we all looked at him, which embarrassed the shit out of him.

"Wait," she said, "that's not the good part. He says to me that he wants to fuck me right there on the money, so I pull the covers down and he climbs up on the money and he starts eating me like crazy, really goin' at it, till all of a sudden he freezes and says, 'DON'T MOVE A MUSCLE!' I thought, *What the hell is happenin?*"

She stopped and giggled and her tits jiggled in front of her. "What happened?" Rob asked.

"He lost his goddamn contact lens!" she howled. "He lost the goddamn thing up my pussy!"

She was a pretty tacky broad, but she sure as hell was funny. She told us how he dug his fingers up her cunt, with one eye closed, looking for his godddamned contact lens! When he finally found it, he put it in his eye and yelled because it burned. "Ever have pussy juice in your eye?" she asked us. "It burns like Murine!"

I could have used some Murine four hours later as we sat in a cell downtown, just me and my boys this time, in a big tank with assorted drags, drunks, and addicts. When they herded us out of the van and into jail, they separated the girl—I think her name was Nellie, I'm not even sure—and her pals from us and we never saw them again. I hope they learned how to fucking park a car.

When we got downtown they realized we hadn't been searched at the precinct station and the cops down there really did a number on us—hands over our cocks, getting their jollies, looking to see what was stuck up our assholes, shoving us around. Taking the money had been a mistake; a cop took it and that was the last I would see of what I thought would be our bail money.

It was such an unpleasant evening (except for the contact-lens story) that I became more and more committed to never allowing it to happen again. And I haven't. A few of my boys have been in trouble but I've been able to buy their way out, and, in some cases, fight the little evidence they had and *win* our way out. It is difficult to bust a call-boy ring, especially if the top guy running the place is on his toes, if he keeps all his books in code and locked away in a vault, if he moves enough and doesn't keep more than two "roommates" in his place, if he is—and this is all it amounts to—one step ahead of the fucking police.

We were hustled into the courtroom about ten o'clock the following morning. Terry, one of my boys, began to get very scared by that time because a cop had hit him hard back at the apartment and his head was beginning to pound. He started to cry and I held him in my arms, which drew laughter from the cops and a derisive bitchery from one of the transvestites in the can. I ignored them and promised Terry it would never happen again, that he would be fine. He had suffered a slight concussion, I found out later, and my doctor (the son of the doctor who had cared for all of us at Helen's place) fixed him up fine.

The courtroom contained a familiar face. Helen sat there, regal, spitting mad, watching. Everyone in the place knew her well and seemed to be almost afraid of her. She was flanked by two lawyers and they came to our aid and hit the judge with a whirlwind of legal-sounding bullshit that blew holes in the case, and he dismissed it.

Later Helen told me the judge had owed her a favor and the lawyers had only spouted their gibberish to convince the court reporter and cops standing around, as if they had any say in the matter anyway. "Wish that bastard was on the bench the night they got me," Helen muttered. "He was in Tahiti, the son of a bitch."

Well, I was sure as hell glad he wasn't in Tahiti that morning.

Prostitution today is different from what it was yesterday. As the world changes, so does the way things work. But even though the "oldest profession in the world" has come of age, has been computerized, so to speak, the

171

basic premise is still there: pleasure for profit. Paying, whether with dollars, rubles, liquor, or plane fare, to have an hour of pleasure, and hour of fun, an hour away from the problems of the world.

Prostitution has survived.

And so have I.

I stayed in the apartment just off the lake with Rob and Billy for seven months. Then I took a trip to California and Hawaii, and then stopped in Florida to meet with Phillip and Brian, who were there for the entire winter, and when I got back I had a new apartment waiting for me. Rob and Billy had successfully completed the move in my absence, this time to an apartment house nearly in the Loop, which was wonderfully convenient.

I stayed there for a good part of 1973, and then, on my birthday two years ago moved again, back north, to an old building which has the flavor of the apartment I loved so much in the Village in New York. Rob and Billy are still with me, though Rob does a lot of "footwork" and isn't at the apartment very often. One day Billy will do what I did—he'll go out on his own because he's good and he'll make it.

Business has grown past my wildest hopes, in fact it was that way by the middle of last year, and I had to put a limit on how many boys, how many customers, how many everything. I'm in the big time and I don't want anything to blow it. On a trip to Aspen the first winter my service was going strong in Chicago, I decided to buy the A-frame cabin, and it's been a good investment, not only because of the ski trade but because it's a great place to send a customer off to with a kid he or she really likes—and they pay through the eyes to have three days alone with their favorite boy, up there in the beautiful Colorado mountains.

I've learned, with the help of a guy who is an IBM expert and the female bank officer, that computers can be helpful things. Thus, I have my own system of coding the names of all my steady customers, what they pay, the boys they prefer, how many times they've had a certain boy, etc., and they are fed into a computer and punched out on cards that the police will never be able to understand.

Speaking of the cops again, I have to be honest and tell you my attitude has changed a bit. There hasn't been a lot of heat on me because I know the right people and all, true, and because I'm ahead of them, true also, but in the past year, again because of the Houston murders, I've helped find runaways and I've often aided the police in seeing that they're cared for. I have done this because I believe in it, not because I want to be called a saint or win medals, but it has helped my reputation with the vice squad. They realize I'm not out to rape little kids, and they're wising up and realizing that maybe I'm not such a social menace after all. A Joey DeFalco I'm not.

To this day I read about busts on houses and on call girls and hustlers on the streets and I sometimes wonder where our heads are at. Don't we have problems a bit more pressing? Like those of the runaway kids? Or the addicts, or the child-beaters, or the street thugs who will murder for a lousy ten bucks? Who poses more of a threat to our moral future, a madam named Helen or someone like Richard Nixon? I really wonder when we're going to get our shit together.

I've had the greatest boys working for me. Some of them are still with me, like Billy, Rob, and Jake, a kid who joined up right after our bust. Some have gone on to other things—school, marriage, sometimes just bumming around the country. They can do as they please, just as long as they please the customers when they're at work. I've had to let some go because they got into drugs too heavily, because they couldn't handle some customers, and, in some cases, because I chose wrong. I guess even seasoned Grant Saxon can have the wool pulled over his eyes by a cunning hustler. But I learned a hell of a lot from Phillip and I've applied it and more to my set-up, and it works. The best part of it all is the relationship I have with my boys—fantastic! We have parties, go to the beach together, have long and deep talks. We're friends first, business partners second, but when business

173

is important, when they're supposed to be pleasing a customer, friendship is second and their work comes first. They're good boys, beautiful boys. I love them.

And I've had—and have—some interesting customers:

The Happy Hooker told you about the different types of men who frequent the New York brothels. I found it interesting to read what Miss Hollander had to say about age groups, and I think I would say I agree with her, because my experience has been much the same. But in ways I differ when looking at different professions, nationalities, and ethnic groups—how good they are in bed, their pleasures, their quirks. I think it necessary to add my feelings in the same line and give you the "hustler version," so to speak:

Bankers are among the best customers of New York madams. Certainly Wall Street is well-populated, and most of the population there is horny. But I think most of them are straight, for money men did not account for even ten percent of Phillip's business, and though today, in Chicago, I have clients who are bankers, they do not make up a sizable majority. Of the bankers I do service, most of them are women—I told you about the senior officer of a famous Chicago banking house; I still screw her. I also service a few wives of men in the banking business.

I find many of my professional categories the same as you would find listed for any all-girl brothel: politicians, doctors and dentists, lawyers, athletes, you name it. But the emphasis, because this is a stud service, is different. I know, because I have always checked with madams and hookers I have known, besides relying on the wisdom and experience of Helen and Phillip.

Businessmen seem to go for girls more than boys; at least businessmen go to whorehouses more in search of women than in search of boys. Their wives are another story. I guess perhaps their loving husbands are so busy watching the stock market during the day and visiting the brothels by night that they do not find the time to fuck their wives. Thus, the women get itchy, and often businessmen have gone to seed long before they should— paunchy stomachs, flabby muscles, hell, all they do is

174

sit behind desks the whole day long—and younger men certainly seem more attractive to the women. Thus, they search out the studs, and they make magnificent customers because they are hot lays. They don't do it often, and when they do they usually have not masturbated or had relations with their husbands for a week or more before visiting their boy—and, Christ, but they are insatiable! There were more of them in New York than in Chicago, the reason being that Wall Street is bigger than LaSalle Street (and I don't mean the part of the street where Helen's used to be, I mean our financial district here in Chicago).

So, I have a few bankers and quite a few bankers' wives as clients, and some clients in related professions, stockbrokers, accountants, business consultants, but they are in the minority. But without them I would never have known the pleasures of Jewish women, especially those from the age of thirty through fifty. That seems to be their prime; they are "ripe" and they're not afraid to wear my boys out, and, in some cases, wear me out.

I have had a few men whom you would not think are the type to pay for the services of studs. Namely, truck drivers, dock workers, sailors, even a garbage man, or "sanitation engineer" as he called himself. These men are usually uneducated and quite rough and burly and I sometimes feel they are spending an entire paycheck on one of my boys, but if that is what they choose to do, who am I to argue? As long as they treat my boys right, they are welcome customers. They are the exception, of course, and I'm always surprised to find out Jimmy or Teryl has spent the night with a man who digs ditches along the Chicago expressways. It is interesting too that many of these men prefer to experiment with anal intercourse. Maybe they can find blow jobs easily, but fucking a boy is another story—or getting fucked themselves. There is one man, the guy I mentioned who works for the sanitation department, and he is rather handsome, big-muscled, not very bright, but very nice. He likes to be fucked in the ass, regularly, once a month. I know garbage men make good money, but certainly not the

175

money a stockbroker rakes in, so I give him a discount rate. The boy he prefers says he's one of his favorite customers.

If they are the exception, what is the rule? Who are the biggest customers? It seems that the people who use the services of studs more than any other are men and women involved in some way with the arts. Actors, actresses, musicians, dancers, artists, sculptors, rock singers, opera stars, drama students, writers, poets, publishers, designers, decorators, filmmakers, composers and lyricists, agents, personal managers, just about anyone connected with the arts in some way, shape, form, or fashion.

They are, of course, my favorite customers, for they are literate, clean, interesting, well-behaved, sensitive, and very experimental—going to bed with them is never boring. They have a certain amount of class, and I like that. They are people you can have a decent conversation with when you've finished having sex. And they are well-seasoned sexual partners, always wanting to try something new, to experiment. Most often, also, they are the best-looking of all my clients, and my boys have often felt their hearts reaching out toward many of the beautiful men and women who have had them. But I give them my warning about never falling in love with a customer, and they usually heed my advice; if not, well, they learn on their own.

Some of my clients do *nothing*, mainly because they are so filthy rich. They often make up the percentage of customers I would consider the most jaded. They find regular sex quite boring, and they are often into the freakiest scenes imaginable. I think their wealth makes them restless, bored with life, too complacent and apathetic, so their energy is put into their sexual drive, and the whips and chains and cock rings and dildoes and vibrators and sexual toys of every description have an important place in their visits to my boys.

I must say that I particularly like customers who have something to do with books, publishing, libraries, literature. But you already know my love for reading and writing, and I guess it is easy to understand why I prefer

176

these people. Some of them are fine in bed (especially one female librarian who likes to be fucked in the ass while a vibrator is stuffed up her pussy) and a few of them tend to be a little bookish, reserved, and almost puritanical in their attitude toward making love, and I usually do my best to ease them into trying new things, new positions, and the like. And you can bet whenever I have a famous author as a customer, whether he or she has written a cook book or a spy novel, I feel a secret thrill. I am sometimes honored to be making love to a genius, which some of the writers I have been to bed with certainly are.

Do I have a few "special" customers today? Yes, as any call boy will always have, if he be a madam or no. I adore my lady bank officer. I see a famous rock composer/singer rather infrequently because of his concert schedule and globe-hopping, but when I do, I could last a week on the high I get from the session. He is one of the "glitter" rock stars who have recently taken the music business by storm, and most people know of his blatent bisexuality. Well, he is, in all truth, completely homosexual. You wonder why he chooses to pay me for my services when there are millions of fans and gay groupies who would drop their pants for him at the snap of a finger? Well, he has been given gonorrhea seven times by adoring fans, and I think he would much rather pay for clean sex than keep having to get his ass shot full of penicillin. Let him get roses and fan letters from the masses, I'll keep him satisfied where it counts.

There is a man-and-wife team I enjoy, and I take vacations with them often, because they own a major part of an airline and are usually hopping from city to city around the world. Often, since they are both bisexual, we will invite a local hooker to join us, and it makes for a wonderful party. They also have the finest collection of fuck films I have ever seen.

(I have heard stories of a famous Hollywood producer —no, not the guy who threw Coke bottles at me in Malibu—who is quite old now and gets his kicks by running his private collection of stag films for friends and guests. What is exceptional about his collection is the stars of his films—no, they're not John Holmes and Georgina Spelvin and Marilyn Chambers. They are real stars whom you pay three bucks to see on the big screen. If you were a friend of the producer, you could be seeing them for free, and in, I'm sure, Academy Award-winning roles. The story of how he amassed this truly remarkable collection of pornographic movies of famous stars is told this way: Whenever a certain actor or actress wanted a major part in one of his films (and all of his films are guaranteed box-office hits) they had to make a little "home movie" first. Simple, neat business deal. The man was a good hustler.)

I have a girl who is quite young and quite lovely. She is only twenty-three, and she was sent to me by her father, who figured she should be taught the ways of sex by someone who knows. I guess he felt that was the thing to do because he had been introduced to sex in a brothel when he was seventeen—his father brought him in. Anyway, I wasn't sure the girl would be ready for something like that, and I told the man I wanted to talk with her first. And I'm glad I did, because she was very apprehensive and afraid that the experience would be a bad one. But she was very bright and she admitted to me that her longing to have intercourse outweighed her apprehension, but she just had never been able to go through with the act because she, like Shelley, had been raised a Catholic, and in her case it was even worse because many of her early years (her mother died in childbirth) had been spent in a convent school. I told her she should wait and think about it, and we planned on meeting the next day for a walk on the beach. This was in California. Her father had flown me there from Aspen just for the purpose of fucking his daughter.

Well, we met the next day, and by the time we had found a little cove we had come to like each other so much that all of her fears subsided, and I made love to her, naked on the beach, in the sun, and it was beautiful for both of us. The man paid me well, but the pleasure was mine. Since that day, she has come back seven or eight times (she is now a stewardess) and likes to pay me for it "because that's the way we first did it."

I must mention here that there is definitely something to be said for California, Hawaii, Bermuda, Puerto Rico, the Mediterranean, anywhere the climate is tropical and the sun is in its glory. I'm saying there is no better place for sex than outdoors! No wonder Brando escapes to Tahiti! I think, if it were possible, the best houses should be run in the outdoors. I don't think a mattress can compare with the thrill of green grass under your naked body and the warmth of the sun or the chill of the wind on your ass. I love vacationing in warm climates (especially in January) and making love with Mother Nature watching. Even here in Chicago, during the summer, I often take a trick to the rooftop (the neighbors get a kick out of that—you should hear some of the phone calls I've received because of *that*) or, if he or she is paying enough, we travel to one of the resorts in southern Wisconsin and find a nice secluded spot in the forest. You would be surprised how many women, especially Jewish housewives who never seem to leave their houses, cars, or temples, freak out when doing it outdoors for the first time.

And I see I'm back to Jewish women again. Oh, there are Italian women, and German women . . .

Let's see what I think of my ethnic patrons:

Italians—The men are always warm and exciting, highly sexed, and often younger than most of my clients, and usually quite striking in appearance. They make wonderful lovers. The women are another story. Though very earthy, they are not imaginative in bed. They often want to be fucked and that's it—they lie there and take it without much reaction. Women who were actually born in Italy are a bit worse. It seems as though they are conditioned to lying on their backs and having children —so what are they doing with a stud service? It still puzzles me. Italians of both sexes seem to prefer blond boys, the exact opposite of their own kind.

English—The British are good at what they do, but they are cold. Flo was the exception; I have never met a British woman who did not take the time to thank me courteously and politely for what was, at least in my eyes, a somewhat mechanical fuck. Things must be "shipshape" to the point one feels Queen Elizabeth herself is going to enter. There is an uptightness about English women I would love to break, and on occasion I have done so. But it isn't easy. The men are even worse, although, again, they are good in bed. However, I cannot warm up to them, and from what my boys tell me, neither can they. One of my studs said, "You know, Grant, when I'm bed with an Englishman, I have the feeling he still has his clothes on!" I think that sums it up. They don't bend easily, they are overly polite, they pay well, and they leave you wondering if you really pleased them. But they come back for more, and that tells you right off that you pleased them. As in all cases, I have found exceptions to the rule, but I would say that this is generally a fair assumption.

Spanish and Mexican—Oh, man, some of these guys and girls are terrific! No wonder Spanish hookers are sometimes called "hot tamales!" I got to know Mexicans, Spaniards, and Chicanos when I lived in California, and there is literally no end to what they can do in bed. The women claw and are the most vocal of all women customers, squealing, moaning, sweating. You get a real workout with one of them, and you end up loving it and hoping she comes back for more. The boys are the same, magnificent lovers, smooth-talking and fast-moving. They give great head and seem to enjoy sucking circumcised cocks more than the uncircumcised variety, because, again like the Italians, it is different from most of their own experience. I enjoy Spanish and Mexican men and women tremendously. In fact, all the customers I have had from South America, Latin America, Spain itself, have been memorable. One drawback: They never want to let go. If they have paid for you, you are theirs forever, or so they seem to think. Just yesterday one of my boys called me and in a worn-out voice asked, "Hey, man, how do I get rid of her?" I think they want to fuck themselves to death.

Scandinavians—They *savor* sex. They have been brought up with it, taught it early in their lives, and seem to always remember that love is part of sex. They seem to want to kiss almost as much as the French do, and they could go on hugging and petting for hours. The men really make *love* to a boy, they do not merely take their money's worth out on his cock. By that I mean they enjoy rolling around in bed, kissing and caressing, and their biggest trip is sucking—they love intercourse, but they seem to be orally inclined first. Even more so with Scandinavian women. They are some of the best cocksuckers on earth, especially the Swedish girls. I think the fact that they are healthy and robust and full of zest, both physically and mentally, has a great deal to do with their love of lovemaking. Oh, what great mouths they have!

French—Kissing is their sport, and not only on the mouth. The women love to be eaten and there seems to be no end to their desire to have a stud's tongue up their cunts. In France itself, the women are not very clean and it takes a while to get used to the hair under their arms (which is true also for women in Spain and Italy) and on their legs. But most of them are becoming more and more Americanized and the trend is changing. French women love to lick a boy's asshole, I have discovered often enough, and while they are sucking a boy's cock they adore finger-fucking him. As for the men, they are as good as the women—kissers, rimmers, fine sexual partners. They are suave and sophisticated, eager to please and be pleased, which is exactly what any good hustler wants. They never quibble about prices.

Dutch—I have been to Holland twice, but as a companion to a non-Dutch client, thus I have no idea what the people there are like in bed. I must say they are a handsome lot, as healthy and happy-looking as the Scandinavians. I have only had one Dutch woman here in America, and she was quite drunk and I'm not sure I should base any observation on her. I have heard from various sources that the homosexuals from Holland are incredible lovers, but whether that is true or not, I do not really know. The next time you fly to Amsterdam, try it and find out for yourself! (And tell me about the women, because I have heard almost nothing about them.)

Hungarians, Yugoslavs, and Czechs—I always think

of the women being fat and wanting to lie on top of the boy, sometimes nearly crushing him to death. They usually have large breasts and adore having the boy fondle and suck them. The men are rather average, sometimes a little rough, but never as rough as the Germans. Often they prefer kinky sex. I've heard tales of a rich Czech who was the son of a Roman Catholic priest who liked to be beaten and then squirted with whipped cream.

Austrians—A bit rougher than the previous group, and not quite as hard to take as the next:

Germans—My God, but their fair skin and blond hair are deceiving! The men are hard to handle, as many of them are strong and forceful, and they seem to enjoy beating people. I find the impression people have of German men making love with an army uniform and whip lying next to the bed a correct one. They often deal in leather and bondage scenes, and they order you around as if you are a prisoner. The women are much like their Austrian and Hungarian counterparts, usually large, big-breasted, eager to fuck. But they too are rougher than most. Many German men and women will refuse to sleep with a circumcised boy, and a good stud service will keep this in mind when they hear the name Freilich over the phone—ask if they prefer them uncut.

Orientals—I have not had many of them myself, but since the Japanese electronics companies have taken over our television and stereo sales, many of my boys service them. In fact, we have a beautiful stereo system in my Chicago apartment which was a gift from the president of one of the well-known Japanese firms. I hear they are warm and kind, and are often ashamed of their small stature and their small penises. I never send them hung boys unless they specify that. One of my boys has a Chinese boyfriend and says he is the best lover he has ever had.

Greeks—Oh, God! If I were truly homosexual with no desire for women at all, I would find a Greek god and stay with him forever. Greek men are by far and away the finest clients in the world. Meaning that they are the best lovers in the world. They are strong, terribly masculine, charming, almost inspiring in some ways. "The

182

Greek Way" is anal intercourse, and spending one night with a Greek tells you how it came to be called that. They love anal sex, and they are true masters of it. Nearly every high-class hooker I've talked to agrees that Greeks are the best. Helen used to give all the best girls to Greek men, as I do with my best boys today. Three of my hustlers are of Greek origin and they are among my most popular boys. Most Greeks have good-sized cocks, and my boys are no exception. Even street hustlers will tell you they prefer Greeks. There is a sexuality in their make-up that can't be beat. As for Greek women, they tend to be like two sides of a coin. On one side you have a fat cow with greasy black hair and you can't imagine her doing anything other than tending goats on a hillside. But, thankfully, on the other side of the coin is Melina Mercouri. Need I say more?

Irish—Working out of Chicago puts me in touch with many Irish, to say the least. We have some of the best times around St. Patrick's Day, when Mayor Daley dyes the Chicago River Kelly green and the entire city goes completely apeshit! I do like the Irish because they enjoy what they are doing, honestly enjoy it, though they often get rowdy and boisterous. The women are easy to please, the men eager to please. Somtimes they are a little skimpy with money—they never leave tips—but they are part of the "flavor" of Chicago, a flavor I love.

Israelis—If you can stand listening to a dissertation on the current situation in Israel and what the Arabs have done lately, you can make it through the night with a tried-and-true Israeli. Both the men and women like to suck cock, but they are not as good as American Jews.

American Jewish—I think if I had kept a list of every trick I have turned in my life, Jews would come up at the top. I do prefer Greek men over Jewish men. I think I prefer a Spanish woman over a Jewish woman. I say "think" because it is a hard statement to make; I love American Jews, as people and as sexual partners. Young Jewish boys are terrific in bed, and I find many of them to be exclusively homosexual. Young Jewish women are not as good as the thirty-to-fifty age group, as I have already stated. But the Jewish men seem to be good until they drop dead. I think part of the reason I like Jews so much is that they pay well, even though bargaining is something one must get used to, just as though you were arguing over the price of Kosher salami in the deli. Another part of the reason is that they're wild and crazy—they're willing to try anything, and they are into the kinkiest and freakiest sex scenes in the world. I've already told you about many of them, and I think I could write a book just on what I've done with Jews, or what I've heard from other hustlers and hookers.

There are other categories beyond ethnic listings:

Housewives—Horny as hell, and I mean housewives with five kids, two cars, a house in the burbs, *Time Magazine* on the coffee table (though I wonder if they ever read it), and trips to the hairdresser each Saturday. Topping all housewives are the Jewish women; poor or rich or middle-class, they're the best, better than single Jewish women or divorced Jewish women or working Jewish women. The horny Jewish housewife is my favorite lay.

The Automotive Industry—This is a category? Oh, yes, it sure as hell is. You wouldn't believe what goes on behind the curtains of the auto shows each year. While the salesmen are out there pushing Gremlins and Mustangs and Monte Carlos, the upper crust of the auto industry is using the services of studs like Grant Tracy Saxon. There is a particular stratum of society bred and fed by Detroit's automotive industry, the Grosse Point crowd. The women are well-bred ex-models and ex-little-rich-girls and ex-actresses (and ex-hookers in two cases I know of) and they wear diamonds while they fuck. But they're hot for it and they do well, no matter what nationality they are. Because Detroit is so close to Chicago, a lot of business comes to me, and my boys often return from the rich Detroit suburbs with enormous smiles on their faces. They loved being greeted at the door of a mansion, ushered to "madam's room" by a black butler, only to find a woman dressed in garter belt and diamond necklace, waiting with open legs. The men are not quite so bizarre, but they pay well—hell,

I got a free car out of the deal once! And both the women and the men seem to be conscious of size, always asking for my biggest boys. I hope the switch to smaller cars does not mean a switch to smaller cocks. Knowing the Detroit crowd, I doubt it.

Women's Libbers—Okay, you don't believe any woman who says she's liberated would be paying for a stud to bang her, do you? I can only tell you what I know. Two months ago, almost to the day, I met a woman at the Drake Hotel here in Chicago and I knew I recognized her but I could not come up with her name, and I knew the one she had given me was false. Just about the time I was sticking my cock up her ass, it came to me. She had been on a talk show recently, spouting liberation for women as loud and clear as Gloria Steinem. She flaunted her lesbianism and told the world she had had it with men. Apparently she had not quite had enough, since she was paying me a hundred bucks to have me kneel behind her and fuck her ass till she cried in pleasure. Later, after we had rested, she started sucking my cock like wildfire and I happened to see three copies of her book (it's a big seller now) which had just been released. It is all about men treating women as sex objects. I don't plan to read it.

Athletes—The women tend to be very dykish and I often wonder if they wouldn't be more satisfied with another girl and a two-way dildo. The men are out to prove their masculinity (although I know a football player who is one of the cuddliest persons I've ever gone to bed with) and sometimes think they are out on the basketball court rather than in bed. And those are *my* balls they're bouncing!

What else?

I have never had a professional stuntman, a female hairdresser, a lion tamer, a woman with three tits, or an Eskimo. I think I have gone through everything else.

Who are the three women in the world whom I'd most like to go to bed with? Julie Christie, 'cause I adore her, a beautiful woman whose name I don't even know, but I've seen her selling cosmetics at Bonwit Teller in the

John Hancock Center, and Julie Nixon Eisenhower, because she needs to be taught a trick or two.

The three men? Warren Beatty, Anthony Armstrong-Jones (or Lord Snowfall, or whatever the Queen calls him now), and Mick Jagger, just to see if that plaster caster was telling the truth.

The people I've raised the prices on in the past year: Oil-company executives. Because I couldn't get gas on my way to Lake Geneva a few months ago and because of the recently released profit reports issued to the public. Those guys and their wives can afford a price hike!

The people who get discounts regularly: Students, women I find attractive and who want me but don't have enough money to afford my regular prices, anyone who owns a gas station, and some ex-Washington government employees, since they have high legal bills to pay and the whole world is down on them.

Customer I have regretted most: Catherine Ann.

Customer I wish I could have again: Eleanor.

My aim right now: not to change a thing. I want to go on doing what I am doing, exactly as I am doing it.

For, you see, I brought "Paris" to Eleanor many years ago, and I've tried my best to do the same for other people since.

I'm a hustler.

I bring pleasure to others and that makes me happy. Why should anyone want to change that?

EPILOGUE

Now I'm twenty-six years old. And, as Helen would say, "This kid's been around." I've met countless men and women, and with my skills I've tried to make their lives a bit brighter by making them happy, putting into very real terms what may have remained only a fantasy for them, sharing in their joys and listening to their problems.

I have found that most people are not very satisfied with their lives, that they are not entirely happy, either with their families or friends, in their jobs, with the style in which they live. By relieving themselves sexually, they are better able to cope with life, and are, at least in a small way, happier. A little happiness is worth a hell of a lot, and if I've been the reason some people have been able to walk around with a smile on their faces, I've done something in this life.

I'm supposed to be rough, seasoned, hard. Isn't that what people expect of a hustler? If that's what they expect, that's what they get. As I said, you give me a scenario, I'll act out any role. But as I've been writing this journal, I've tried to be myself. It was hard to hold back writing a hundred pages about Shelley, and it was even harder to mention her at all. To know you once loved a girl and still do and will never see her again is a difficult thing to put down on paper. I couldn't be the "seasoned stud of the world" there and pretend my relationship with her didn't affect me. I'm sure it has come across that I loved Kent all these years with a love that is not your buddy-to-buddy friendship variety. Hustlers aren't supposed to admit something like that, either. And, in a different way from anyone else, I loved Flo.

But what are we? Machines? I object to the idea that prostitutes, male and female, are nothing more than sexual robots. I'm almost six feet tall, my hair is sandy brown, I have green eyes, I dress in faded jeans, and I have a big cock. But I've got a heart and feelings too, and whether or not my customers understand it, the real reward in this business comes from seeing someone pleased, and this is what I want *you* to know. I've read too many life stories of Robbie; I've heard all too often tales of the hooker who ends up with a needle in her arm. It isn't the rule, and if I've destroyed your impression that we're basically bad people, that we hurt people, that we're all sinners of one sort or another, then I've succeeded with this book.

I think the reason Miss Pearl lived so long is that she wanted to. And why? The answer lies in one of her letters: "Tracy, I'm an old woman, but I feel as young as I was the day my mammy told me I was gonna work in the big white house on the plantation. Lot of people, they didn't like working for whites, but Pearl liked working for anybody, because I just like about everybody. I looooooove people, my Tracy, I like seeing what makes 'em tick. I keep dragging this old body around with me 'cause I want to see what's gonna happen next year. I want to be there. I don't want to miss it! And if you keep loving living and seeing what people are gonna do next, if you keep making all them folks happy and they make you happy too, Tracy, you are going to outlive old Miss Pearl. You know, son, I hate to go to sleep at night sometimes because I get scared I might miss something while my eyes are closed."

I'll tell her whole story some other day.

But in that paragraph I think she told a good part of mine.

I've got to end this because I think there is nothing more to tell, at least not today, and also because I've got

188

a very beautiful and very rich lady waiting for me in the other room. She's new and I just saw her come in and Rob stuck his head in the door and said, "She's a hot one."

Hot or cold, it won't really matter. I'm going to have fun.

Later,

Grant or Tracy
(whichever you prefer!)

MORE BESTSELLERS FROM
WARNER PAPERBACK LIBRARY

MALEVIL by Robert Merle   **(79-685, $1.95)**
This is the powerful and provocative novel by the author of **The Day of the Dolphin.** Twenty-three weeks an international bestseller! In an isolated French chateau, a group of friends have gathered. While they taste the wine in the deep cellar, a nuclear explosion incinerates the earth. They are survivors, Robinson Crusoes of a dead world, condemned to go back to man's roots and reinvent the means of existence.

MARILYN by Norman Mailer   **(71-850, $2.50)**
Norman Mailer, winner of the Pulitzer Prize and National Book Award, views Marilyn Monroe, sex goddess, superstar and vulnerable child woman. COMPLETE WITH COLOR PICTURES.

THE WAR BETWEEN THE TATES   **(79-813, $1.95)**
by Alison Lurie
Fourteen weeks on **The New York Times** bestseller list! The brilliant, witty novel of a marriage under siege by young sex, middle age and old dreams. "A thing to marvel at . . . all that the novel was meant to be."—**The New York Times**

THE PALACE GUARD   **(79-918, $1.95)**
by Dan Rather and Gary Paul Gates
America's number one bestseller! "In this fascinating recapitulation of the Nixon years . . . Rather and Gates tell why there was such a thing as Watergate . . . with marvelous insight and back-door scholarship and at a galloping pace that exhilarates."—**San Francisco Examiner**

 A Warner Communications Company

Please send me the books I have checked.

Enclose check or money order only, no cash please. Plus 25¢ per copy to cover postage and handling. N.Y. State residents add applicable sales tax.

Please allow 2 weeks for delivery.

WARNER PAPERBACK LIBRARY
P.O. Box 690
New York, N.Y. 10019

Name ....

Address ....

City .... State .... Zip ....

———— Please send me your free mail order catalog

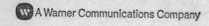

MORE GREAT READING FROM
WARNER PAPERBACK LIBRARY